THE
CROSS
EXAMINATION
of JESUS CHRIST

AND

THE
CROSS
EXAMINATION
of OLIVER FINNEY

RANDY SINGER

WATERBROOK
PRESS

THE
CROSS
EXAMINATION
of JESUS CHRIST

RANDY SINGER

WATERBROOK
PRESS

THE CROSS EXAMINATION OF JESUS CHRIST
PUBLISHED BY WATERBROOK PRESS
12265 Oracle Boulevard, Suite 200
Colorado Springs, Colorado 80921
A division of Random House Inc.

Details in some anecdotes and stories have been changed to protect the identities of the persons involved.

Praise for
The Cross Examination of Jesus Christ

"Randy Singer is not only a talented lawyer, but he is also a gifted writer. In his latest work, Randy provides a thought-provoking look at the cross-examination of Jesus that is absolutely a must-read."
—JAY SEKULOW, chief counsel, the American Center
for Law and Justice

"Randy Singer is a brilliant and creative communicator for Jesus Christ. He uses his unique background as a trial lawyer and a missions executive to bring a fresh perspective to our understanding of the Savior."
—STEVE DOUGLASS, president of Campus Crusade for Christ
International and author of *Enjoying Your Walk with God*

"Randy Singer has sung! Here is a wonderful apologetic resource for saint and skeptic alike. Saints will find their faith encouraged and strengthened, while skeptics will be seriously challenged to consider the Christian faith. The book combines a blend of pertinent information, cogent logic, humor, and penetrating biblical insights, all of which serve the reader extremely well. Be ready to experience the best of Christian communication in *The Cross Examination of Jesus Christ*."
—DR. PHIL ROBERTS, president of Midwestern Baptist
Theological Seminary

"*The Cross Examination of Jesus Christ* is a powerful book that combines the varied and rich gifts and expertise of its author, Randy Singer. Combining his legal experience and knowledge with his theological depth and his gift of writing, this book will move readers further along in their faith. Grab *The Cross Examination of Jesus Christ* and be entertained, enlightened, and shaken to the core—all at once!"

—KAREN COVELL, television producer, author of *How To Talk About Jesus Without Freaking Out* and *The Day I Met God,* and director of the Hollywood Prayer Network

"The most unique, compelling, and powerful look at the trial and death of Jesus that I have ever seen. Those who love Jesus will love Him more. Those who doubt Jesus will face the challenge of their lives. And no one who reads it will remain unchanged."

—JOHN AVANT, vice president of evangelization at the North American Mission Board and author of *The Passion Promise* and *Authentic Power*

"Jesus is cross-examined by every generation. He is questioned publicly but more often privately in our thoughts, where our skepticism, ignorance, and fears compete with our conscience, our highest hopes, and our desire for truth. Thankfully, every generation produces a talented author, with a passion for truth, who is skilled in marshaling the evidence concerning what Jesus taught and who Jesus is. Randy Singer is such a person. His book, *The Cross Examination of Jesus Christ,* is a very readable, informative, and self-revealing summation of the timeless, incomparable, yet always compelling answers Jesus gives to the decisive questions about God and us. Singer calls for us to read the book and render our verdicts on Jesus in the manner by which we choose to live our daily lives. Read the book. Render your verdict. It will likely change your life."

—SAMUEL B. CASEY, executive director and CEO of the Christian Legal Society

THE
CROSS
EXAMINATION
of JESUS CHRIST

To Bob Reccord—mentor and friend.

*Thanks for believing that God could use
even a lawyer in the ministry.*

Contents

Acknowledgments xi

Introduction: A Dangerous Witness 1

1.   Rome v. Jesus of Nazareth (The Trial) 9

2.   Who Can Forgive Sins but God? 31

3.   Bloody Band-Aids and Telltale Hearts 47

4.   What's Your Sign? 65

5.   Guilty as Sin 91

6.   The Law as Taskmaster 105

7.   Jesus Takes the Fifth 127

8.   Making Heads and Tails of Church and State 151

9.   The Witness Strikes Back 169

10.   Rome v. Jesus of Nazareth (The Verdict) 189

Notes 203

ACKNOWLEDGMENTS

Writing a book about Jesus is life changing. Studying His life in the detail necessary to research this book has been one of the most convicting and insightful experiences I've had. Accordingly, I want to begin by thanking my Savior for living the kind of life—and dying the kind of death—that continues to inspire, renew, and transform us two thousand years later.

But writing a book about Jesus is also nerve-racking. After all, if I make a mistake about one of my fictional characters, they'd be hard pressed to complain since I created them. But writing about the central figure in all human history…well, that's a whole different story. Literally.

My solution? Pray hard and lean harder than ever on those who provide invaluable expertise and help. It starts with the best advanced reading team in the business. Thanks to Robin Pawling, Michael Garnier, Keith Singer, and Rhonda Singer for their astute insights and delicate chain-saw surgery on the early drafts. Thanks also to Dr. John Avant, vice president of evangelism at the North American Mission Board of the Southern Baptist Convention, for helping me wrestle through some of the theological issues, and to Rev. Wayne Patterson for his objective feedback on some critical issues.

Next came my world-class editing team, including Dudley Delffs, Eric Stanford, and Laura Wright, who helped me focus the book and lop off another twenty thousand words with their slightly smaller chain saws. After that, they broke out the scalpels for wordsmith surgery on what was left. I cannot adequately express what a blessing it is to have editors who care as much about the book as these folks do.

And then there's my family—Rhonda, Rosalyn, and Joshua—the suffering saints in the process. They helped sharpen ideas and provided feedback on an ongoing basis. And, when I needed a computer-generated design to illustrate a key point, Joshua came through on that as well.

A special thanks to my readers who are willing to check out what a fiction writer–lawyer has to say about the very Son of God. My prayer is that He might somehow redeem the words of this lawyer, the same way He did with those who questioned Him, for the purpose of drawing people closer to Himself.

Introduction

A DANGEROUS WITNESS

Cross-examination," said noted jurist John Wigmore, "is the greatest legal engine ever invented to discern the truth."[1] Never has that engine performed more flawlessly than it did during the life of Christ, generating the most powerful truths in the history of the world. This book is the story of Jesus on the witness stand—His jaw-dropping answers that shocked the Pharisees and inspire us still. Nobody had to administer Christ the oath: "Do you swear or affirm to tell the truth, the whole truth, and nothing but the truth, so help you God?" He was God. He *is* God. And He is *truth*.

The purpose of this book, like the purpose of any effective cross-examination, is to reveal the truth—not just what Jesus taught but who Jesus is. His character. His intellect. His mission. The astounding depth of His love.

Our verdict will be a lifestyle more like His.

CROSS-EXAMINATION 101

Cross-examination, my professors stressed, is the most dangerous part of any trial. A slippery witness can decimate your case before you know what has happened. That's why you never ask a question if you don't already know the answer. The classic illustration goes something like this:

> LAWYER (defending someone accused of assault): You didn't actually see my client bite the nose of the alleged victim. Isn't that true?
>
> WITNESS: That's true.
>
> LAWYER: In fact, at the time of the alleged incident, there were several people engaged in a fight and your view of the victim was blocked. Isn't that true?
>
> WITNESS: Yes.
>
> LAWYER: Then how can you be so sure that it was my client who bit the victim's nose as opposed to one of the other men in the fight?
>
> WITNESS: Because I saw him spit it out.

By then, it's too late to plea-bargain.

Another thing to keep in mind, according to those same professors, is the difference between a dangerous witness and one who can't really hurt you very much. With a dangerous witness, sometimes the best cross-examination is no cross-examination at all.

But the Pharisees didn't go to my law school. So they hurled the most volatile questions possible at the most dangerous witness of all time without knowing what the answer might be. The explosions reverberate still.

If you were expecting this book to be intellectual brain candy—
Christ matching wits with the Pharisees while we all cheer—put it
down. It's far more dangerous than that, more like a stick of dynamite
than cotton candy. You can't watch these confrontations from a distance. Christ will draw you in and convict you, causing you to reeval-
uate the way you think and live. You'll smirk at Christ the agitator.
Stand in awe of Christ the revolutionary. Marvel at Christ the
philosopher. And fall deeper in love with Christ the Savior.

DO WE REALLY NEED ANOTHER BOOK ABOUT JESUS?

One could argue that even a million more books about Jesus would
never cover the breadth of His character or the depth of His grace.
Under this view there could never be too many books about the central figure in all of history.

But I'll take a different approach. I wrote this book not just to
add another voice to the choir, but to look at Jesus from a unique
angle that is immensely revealing though largely ignored. It is the
story of Christ under the withering fire of cross-examination, and
it is organized and narrated differently than any book you've ever
read.

The first and last chapters are a firsthand account of the final trial
of Jesus—historical fiction based on scriptural fact. Together, those
chapters tell the story of the greatest miscarriage of justice ever, bar
none. I've placed you there as Pontius Pilate's primary legal advisor—
the *assessore* who would have advised Pilate under the Roman legal
system. The book's middle eight chapters flash back to Christ's explosive confrontations with the Pharisees, examining eight of the most

intense episodes between Jesus and His critics. These exchanges, perhaps better than any others, reveal the heart and mind of Christ. We return, in the final chapter, to Pilate's court, to the verdict of the Romans, and ultimately to the cross.

I've used this organization—first-person fiction bracketing the eight nonfiction chapters—for both a spiritual reason and a practical one. The spiritual reason is this: when Christ came to town, He taught the greatest truths of all time using the two methods I've tried to emulate in this book. First, Jesus told stories. And second, He answered questions from skeptics. He didn't preach three-point sermons with soft music playing in the background. He faced relentless cross-examination. And He talked about wedding feasts and farmers sowing seeds and good Samaritans. He used fictional characters to convey life-changing truths. That's the spiritual reason the book is organized this way.

So what's the practical side of it?

I'm a fiction writer and a former trial lawyer. This is what I do; it's how I communicate. Trial lawyers are storytellers. We believe in the mantra of all novelists: show, don't tell. I want you to experience the intensity and feel the injustice of Jesus's final cross-examination. To do this, I've used fiction to make you part of the story. After all, He went to the cross for *us*.

But trial lawyers aren't just storytellers. We also love cross-examination. Why? Because it forces the jury to choose sides. Though jurors swear to keep an open mind, trial lawyers know that on a subconscious level jurors cannot remain neutral. The more intense the cross-examination, the greater the difficulty. Before the witness ever steps down from the stand, the jurors have decided whether to take the witness at his word or not.

And so will we.

WHO CARES ABOUT THE QUESTIONS ASKED BY THE PHARISEES?

Give the Pharisees and lawyers at least this much credit: they asked the right questions. They asked tough questions on issues that go to the core of Christianity. Those questions still resonate two thousand years later. Questions like the following:

- What proof did Jesus have that He was the Messiah?
- Why did He defend the woman caught in adultery?
- Where do you draw the line between church and state?
- What does it take to be saved?
- What is truth?

The Jesus we find answering these questions may surprise us. If cross-examination does anything, it reveals the character and beliefs of a witness. Jesus was cross-examined for three solid years. These relentless confrontations reveal a Jesus who is at once more tender yet tougher than the one I cut my teeth on in Sunday school.

Tender, as shown by the sensitive way He handled the woman caught in adultery, someone we might condemn if she were dragged into our church sanctuaries today. Tender, in the way He couldn't resist healing on the Sabbath, His love for the crippled overriding His desire to avoid the criticism of the religious leaders.

But tougher in the way He handled His critics. Jesus wasn't afraid to step on toes. In fact, He stomped on them, calling the religious leaders "hypocrites," "blind guides," and "whitewashed tombs." He overturned their money tables and the chairs of those selling doves at the temple. He didn't mince words in His prophecies: "Whoever falls on this stone [meaning Himself] will be broken to pieces; but on whomever it falls, it will grind him to powder!" (Matthew 21:44).

We may find that we've gilded Jesus with so much compassion and sensitivity that His combative side will shock us. But this is the true Jesus, the one revealed on cross-examination. A Savior strong enough to meet His enemies head-on but so tender that He could never resist the desperate pleas of the needy.

And it's not just the unimpeachable *character* of Christ that is revealed on the witness stand. There are also a few surprises and a fair amount of convicting power in what He said.

The key is to put aside our biases and evaluate Christ's teachings at face value, as if we're hearing them for the first time. This is not easy. Our tendency is to twist and torture His words so they fit our preconceived notion of what He should have said or what we wish He had said or what others have told us He said.

Which is, of course, the same fatal mistake made by the Pharisees and lawyers. They couldn't stomach the real meaning of the Mosaic Law, so they tempered the commands of God with the traditions of men. In a similar manner, today we have a hard time swallowing the plain meaning of the words of Christ, so we water down what He said and explain away anything that goes radically against our culture and traditions. It's almost as if we assume that Christ would never really call us to do anything too outrageous.

But He did.

He hung out with the lowlifes—tax collectors and sinners. He defended a woman caught in the act of adultery. He had the audacity to forgive sins, claiming that He would one day sit at the right hand of God the Father. In the parable of the good Samaritan, He attacked the racial bigotry of His day and called for outrageous sacrifices for those in need. He destroyed the legal distinctions between actions and thoughts, calling those of us who have lusted "adulterers" and those who have been angry without cause "murderers."

It's hard to read these radical statements of Christ without subconsciously churning out excuses and rationalizations that protect our comfortable lifestyles. My prayer is that we will take Christ at His word. Unvarnished. Unfiltered. Unaffected by the gloss of traditionalism and our own preconceived ideas. We will let the radical revolutionary speak straight to our hearts, revealed in all His transforming power through the heat of cross-examination.

You Look Vaguely Familiar...

A strange and uncomfortable thing happened as I began writing this book. The more I studied Christ's confrontations with the Pharisees, the more I recognized myself in some of these questioners.

I discovered that some of these folks really loved God but tried to show it with activity rather than relationship. A holy busyness—that felt familiar. I found men who believed that Jesus was obligated to answer all of their *why* questions. There were men so focused on winning arguments that they couldn't hear the cry of a heart. And others who would not be satisfied unless Christ showed Himself powerful through one more miraculous sign or a political conquest or another physical healing. I found religious leaders who didn't spend much time with those outside their own circle of friends, who never dined with tax collectors and sinners.

At times I felt as if I had stepped into this book and started questioning Jesus too.

The thought rocked me like a Mike Tyson right hook in his heyday, before he traded boxing for ear biting. *I'm a lot more like the Pharisees than I ever thought.* Than I ever wanted to be. I tend to interpret Christ's words in light of my own traditions and preconceptions. I'm inclined to put my own self-justifying gloss on the stories of Jesus and the religious leaders. I may feel a need to water Him down or explain Him away or claim that He is speaking symbolically. All of this is the mind-set of a Pharisee, the nitpicking of a lawyer.

That's when I discovered this mind-bending truth: if I want to be like Jesus, I must first realize how much I am already like the Pharisees. In God's paradoxical way, that humbling realization is the first step toward becoming less like the Pharisees we loathe and more like the Savior we love. All of our mental gymnastics and convoluted questions can't make it any other way.

Tricky business, and dangerous, this road toward the mind of Christ. The devil is still a crafty cross-examiner, twisting the truth and distorting the testimony. Like Mike Tyson *after* his prime, Satan couldn't land many direct punches on Christ, but he still had a nasty bite. At the cross, hell bit off more than it could chew.

"How do you know?" you ask (violating the cardinal rule of cross-examination).

"Because three days later they saw hell spit Him out."

1

ROME V. JESUS OF NAZARETH (THE TRIAL)

Y ou have never seen Joseph of Arimathea like this. For one thing, your Jewish friend has never before pounded on your door at sunrise. For another, he's never been this distraught. You thought nothing could rattle this sophisticated member of the great Sanhedrin. He's been a mentor of sorts, helping you figure out this strange Judean culture in the last few years. But this morning he's wild-eyed, refusing to even have a seat.

"They're taking Him to Pilate as we speak," Joseph says between short, hard breaths. "Pilate will summon you soon."

You furrow your brow and try to clear the cobwebs that have gathered overnight. While the Jews prepared for Passover, you celebrated in Roman style—a little too much wine and a long night in the baths. "The same man you hailed as a Caesar a few short days ago?"

"Yes. His name is Jesus. He's a good man, a prophet."

"It seems there are mixed opinions on that."

Joseph scowls. He doesn't seem to appreciate your sarcasm this early in the morning. In the distance you can hear the clamor of the procession moving through the city streets. "The people love Him, Octavian. But the chief priests are threatened by Him. He overturned the moneychangers in the temple—"

"Yes, I heard."

"And condemned the entire religious establishment. They see their lives of luxury slipping away."

"They?" Last time you checked, Joseph was a member of the same "establishment."

Joseph sighs and reaches for your arm. "Octavian, I've never asked you for anything but your friendship. But I'm asking now." His pleading eyes are unsettling. "Jesus of Nazareth is innocent. Don't let Pilate condemn Him."

You don't need this. Not at this hour of the morning. "Okay. What are the charges?"

Joseph blows out a deep "Are you ready for this?" breath. "He claims He's the Son of God," says Joseph, somehow managing a straight face.

If you didn't have such great respect for your friend, you would probably laugh. *Don't we all,* you want to say. But you know that the Jews take their religion very seriously. Joseph has told you all about the coming Messiah. And Joseph is obviously in no mood for wit. For some reason he's got guilt written all over his face.

"I'll change and we'll talk on the way over," you say. "No sense waiting on the summons." You place your hand on top of Joseph's. He's a decent man—one you'll miss when you head back to Rome.

"Pilate won't condemn a man for blasphemy. We've got enough real criminals to contend with."

You're surprised to see tears welling in your friend's eyes. "Please hurry," he manages.

The Sanhedrin's Kangaroo Court

You walk quickly on the way to the praetorium, Pilate's private palace in Jerusalem, making mental notes as Joseph provides a running commentary. The sun is beginning to show its strength in the eastern sky. Across the city the smell of hot cooking grease competes with the stench of garbage in the small alleys and the odor of burning animal flesh from the morning sacrifices.

As Pilate's young assessore, a legal advocate advising the procurator, you focus on the procedural issues. What you hear is appalling, even for this tumultuous province of the Roman Empire. You remind yourself that in two years your posting in Jerusalem will be over and you can return to the grandeur of Rome.

It quickly becomes apparent that the Jewish "trial" was a farce. They arrested Jesus last night and hauled Him before Annas, the former high priest and father-in-law of the current high priest. It's no secret that Annas still rules the Jewish religious hierarchy.

After Annas interrogated Him, they convened the Great Sanhedrin in the middle of the night, Joseph explains. He ticks off the procedural shortcomings on his fingers. It was a nighttime trial, which is prohibited by Jewish law. No public notice of the charges were posted in the temple or sent to the Romans. (You take particular note of this point, remembering other times when the procurator sent you to intervene at the outset of a trial by asserting Roman jurisdiction.)

Joseph continues: The former high priest was allowed to prosecute. Jesus wasn't given a *balil rib*, a court-appointed advocate. The witnesses weren't sworn in and reminded that false testimony would earn them the same punishment they sought for the prisoner. Witnesses contradicted each other, which should have resulted in an instant not-guilty verdict. Jesus was asked questions, a violation of the Talmud's right against self-incrimination.[1]

You've heard enough. Your friend might be emotional right now, but still you need to know. "Joseph, with all due respect—you're a member of the Sanhedrin. Why didn't *you* object? Why bring this fiasco into our courts?"

Joseph remains silent for several steps, his eyes fixed on the ground in front of him. "I've asked myself that a hundred times," he says softly. "I never dreamed Jesus would really need my help. I've seen Him annihilate these same questioners on prior occasions with unearthly wisdom. Honestly, I guess I just expected a miracle." He walks a few more steps. "Still do, in some ways."

You don't believe in miracles, so you stick to the procedural issues. "What did Jesus say?"

"That's just it. He didn't say much of anything. Annas finally got some witnesses to testify that Jesus had threatened to tear down the temple and rebuild it in three days without human hands, though even they couldn't agree on when He had allegedly said it. The whole time, Jesus didn't utter a word."

You turn a corner and see the praetorium ahead, and you're surprised by the size of the crowd. You get a sick feeling in the pit of your stomach as you consider the unpredictable way Pilate handles pressure.

"Did Jesus give *any* testimony?" you ask. You stop walking for a moment so you can clear your mind and develop a strategy before you step onto the stage of public scrutiny.

"Caiaphas placed Jesus under oath and asked if He were the Son of the living God. Jesus replied, 'You have said it.'"

You raise an eyebrow at that. Interesting response. Pretty clever, really.

"But then Jesus went on to say, 'In the future you will see the Son of Man seated at the right hand of the Power and coming on the clouds of heaven.'"

Joseph looks worried. You survey the crowd ahead of you—temple soldiers, the Sanhedrin, a number of black-robed priests. You assume that Jesus is somewhere in the middle of them.

Joseph continues with his commentary: "The chief priest tore his clothes and yelled, 'He has blasphemed! Why do we still need witnesses? Look, now you've heard the blasphemy! What is your decision?' Everyone started yelling that Jesus deserved death."

Joseph drops his voice in shame. "They started hitting Him and spitting on Him. We adjourned court for a few hours and then reconvened at sunrise to render the verdict."

"What was the vote?"

"Unanimous."

Perhaps you've misjudged your friend. You never expected Joseph of Arimathea to give in to mob rule. "Unanimous?"

"Our law contains a proviso that a unanimous verdict of guilt— all seventy-one Sanhedrin members seeing it exactly the same way—

presupposes bias or a setup on the part of the court. A unanimous verdict is supposed to result in an immediate acquittal."[2]

You can't resist a smile at this. Legal loopholes are your specialty. Joseph went along with the others, thinking his guilty vote would actually spring Jesus. "But?"

"But apparently all these religious leaders, who take such great pride in following every jot and tittle of the law, let their hatred of Jesus overpower their love for the law."

"Mmm," you say in response. You start walking again and Joseph joins you. The scene up ahead is turning chaotic. Pilate has yet to appear. The prisoner is surrounded by a wedge of temple guards brandishing swords and shields that glisten in the morning sun. The angry crowd is swelling by the minute, but apparently no one has entered the praetorium to discuss the matter with Pilate. The Jews will not defile themselves by entering a Gentile's house on the day before Passover.

"You really respect this man, don't you, Joseph?"

Joseph answers with his eyes straight ahead, still walking. "I believe He's our Messiah, Octavian. I respect Him, yes. But it's more than that." He hesitates, seemingly unsure of whether he should continue. "I've waited my entire life for Him. My people have waited hundreds of years. 'Respect' does not come close to describing my admiration for this man."

You think about this for a moment but don't have much time for theology right now. Messiah or not, the man deserves a fair trial. You pat Joseph on the shoulder, tell him you'll do what you can, and then begin working your way through the raucous crowd.

Last night at the baths seems like a lifetime ago.

Procedural Skirmishes

A compromise has been reached. The Jews' annoying insistence on not defiling themselves by entering the praetorium (an insult you think Pilate abides too easily) has resulted in a makeshift court being assembled on the marble portico, an immense and elevated porch with imposing Roman colonnades, statues of imperial gods, and a bust of Emperor Augustus, grandfather of Pilate's strong-willed wife, Claudia Procula. The praetorium enjoys the highest elevation on the western hills of the city. From its portico you can look out over the fortress courtyard, the temple courtyards, the lower city, and the neighboring palace for Herod Antipas, intentionally constructed on a slightly lower but adjacent hill.

Pilate takes his place in his imposing judge's chair, an ornately carved wooden throne that has been brought to the portico for this morning's proceedings. You take your seat behind him and to his right. The Sanhedrin, the temple guard, and their captive assemble at the bottom of the stairs, allowing Pilate and his entourage of palace guards to tower over them. The throng of temple sympathizers is growing, but you take comfort in looking at the enormous walls of the Antonia Fortress that surround this courtyard, with scores of soldiers in full battle dress forming rank on its towers and battlements. Rome is in control here; there is no doubt about that.

The defendant is thrust forward, and you find yourself mesmerized. He is Judean, all right, with a dark olive complexion and the sinewy build of a laborer. You are struck by the contrast between His bearing—comfortable, unbent, almost regal—and His appearance. His hands are bound behind His back, and His face carries the marks of the beating described by Joseph. His lips and nose are swollen, gashes cover His forehead and cheeks, and His long, dark hair is matted with blood and sweat. A dark bruise has formed under one eye. Dried blood and spittle are caked on His beard. His robe has been torn so that it hangs awkwardly on one side, revealing welts and bruises on His shoulder and arm. He is chained around the neck like a dog, His captors yanking on the chain to move Him.

He catches His balance, then stands with a quiet dignity. His penetrating brown eyes calmly follow Pilate's every move.

The procurator stands and moves to the edge of the porch. "What charge do you bring against this man?" He poses the question in Greek, the official language of the imperial legal system.

Caiaphas, the burly high priest, steps forward, his eyes burning with contempt. "If this man weren't a criminal, we wouldn't have handed Him over to you." The crowd murmurs its approval.

You shift in your seat. What arrogance! *Just sanction our verdict. Presume we acted correctly. How dare you challenge the Sanhedrin?*

How dare they treat *Rome* with such contempt!

Pilate glances back at you, his round eyes seeking counsel, an unusual move for the confident procurator. You give him a quick shake of the head. He turns slowly back to the crowd. The defendant has not moved. This Jesus shows no signs of the normal trepidation you have seen from those whose lives are in the palm of Pilate's unsteady hand. "Take Him yourselves and judge Him according to your law," Pilate says with a dismissive wave. He takes his seat, signaling an end to the proceedings.

It will not be that easy.

The leaders in the crowd all begin talking at once, surging forward to the bottom of the steps, virtually surrounding the unmoving defendant. They stop clamoring as the voice of Annas rises above the rest. "It is not legal for us to put anyone to death!" he declares angrily. His voice is trembling with rage. The others shout their approval.

Pilate raises a hand and the noise subsides. He surveys the crowd and then looks directly at the defendant. "Bring Him back," Pilate says to the guards. He bolts from his throne and into his headquarters. You follow on his heels.

I Was Born for This

Pilate dismisses the soldiers who have dragged Jesus into the room by the chain around His neck. Jesus seems to fill the entire room. He's the one with His hands manacled, the steel chain hanging from His neck, but it still feels like He's in complete control. He handles Himself like...well, like a Roman. *More like a Roman than Pilate,* you're thinking.

Pilate circles around the prisoner once, looking Him over, while Jesus stares straight ahead. "Are You the King of the Jews?" Pilate asks.

It's a mocking question, considering the poor man's appearance. But you want to give the procurator the benefit of the doubt. Maybe he's just trying to elicit a straightforward denial.

Jesus does not break eye contact. "Are you asking this on your own, or have others told you about Me?"

You suppress a smile at this wily defendant. Hearsay. Jesus is highlighting the fact that Pilate is operating completely on hearsay. Has the procurator seen any evidence that Jesus is trying to establish a kingdom that competes with Caesar? Of course not.

17

"I'm not a Jew, am I?" Pilate retorts. You notice how the round cheeks flush and the V-shaped wrinkles form on his forehead. Pilate's temper is legendary. "Your own nation and the chief priests handed You over to me. What have You done?" Pilate raises his voice for emphasis and closes in on his captive.

But Jesus doesn't shrink back. He answers calmly, deliberately— as if He's explaining something to one of His followers. One of His *slow* followers. "My kingdom is not of this world. If My kingdom were of this world, My servants would fight so that I wouldn't be handed over to the Jews. As it is, My kingdom does not have its origin here."

Pilate considers this for a moment. He seems to realize that Jesus cannot be bullied. "You are a king then?"

"You say that I'm a king. I was born for this, and I have come into the world for this: to testify to the truth. Everyone who is of the truth listens to My voice."

Pilate looks Jesus up and down, as if he's regarding some visitor from another planet. You don't like the direction this is heading. Jesus is talking religion. But Pilate is an eminently practical man, one motivated primarily by his own political ambitions. Religion is a foreign language to him.

"What is truth?" asks Pilate with a snort. And before Jesus can answer, Pilate calls the guards to take the prisoner away. You are left behind to plead His case.

"The man is arrogant," Pilate says as soon as Jesus leaves the room.

"He's also innocent, Your Excellency."

Pilate grunts. "He claims to be a king."

"But you heard Him. He says His kingdom is not of this world."

You're wondering how far you can push this. A man's life is at stake, but Pilate doesn't like to be told what to do. You try to give him an out. "He also claims to be the Son of God—have you heard about that? He's delusional, Your Excellency, but that's not a capital crime."

Pilate walks to the window and looks out at the city, his hands behind his back. "Maybe He is the Son of God," Pilate says, sarcasm dripping from his words. "Maybe we're all crazy and He's the only sane one."

"The Sanhedrin tried Him for blasphemy. That's why they wouldn't tell you the charges. They knew you wouldn't put a man to death for that." You're talking to Pilate's back, your words rebounding with no apparent impact. You find yourself wondering why you care so much about this case. On a deeper level, though, you know. You've always been attracted to the oppressed, the powerless ones. It's probably why they assigned you to this province in the first place—to get you out of Rome for a few years.

"They tried Him in the middle of the night, with perjured testimony," you continue. "They convicted Him at the break of dawn and then roughed Him up before they brought Him to you. It's an internal political squabble, Your Excellency. There's no threat to Rome here."

"It's not Rome I'm worried about," Pilate says to the window. He doesn't elaborate, but you know exactly what he means.

One of his first acts as procurator, even before you were assigned to the province, was to display the image of the emperor on all the standards flying over public buildings in Jerusalem, including the Antonia Fortress, a short distance from the temple. Though these same standards and insignias were displayed elsewhere in the empire, there had always been an understanding that Jerusalem would be an exception, because the Jews believed they constituted idol worship.

Incensed, hundreds of Jewish leaders marched from Jerusalem to Caesarea (Pilate's normal residence except during major festivals). Pilate refused to grant them an audience, so they surrounded his palace and chanted prayers for five days.

When his patience wore thin, Pilate agreed to meet with the Jewish leaders in the amphitheater, allegedly for negotiation. It turned out to be a clever trap—Pilate's soldiers surrounded the crowd, and he threatened to behead them all if they didn't cease and desist. Instead of capitulating, the Jewish leaders demonstrated their willingness to die for the cause, baring their necks and prostrating themselves before the sword-wielding soldiers.

Pilate backed down, agreeing to a face-saving proposal to move the banners to a more appropriate part of his province. On at least two occasions since then, the fanatical Jews forced Pilate to compromise. Once his conduct drew the wrath of Caesar. Pilate knows, as you do, that it can't happen again.

When he turns, his shoulders are slouched forward and his round face is somber. He heads for the door. "He may have to endure a scourging," Pilate mumbles on the way by you.

You know he's not looking for a debate, but the notion repulses you. You've witnessed the brutality of a scourging too many times. Plus your whole life has been devoted to the law—to justice. Men like Pilate come and go, but the majesty of the law is Rome's gift to the world.

"Scourging an innocent man would be unprecedented," you say.

Pilate stops, turns, and pins you back with bloodshot eyes. You fear that you may have crossed the line. He does, after all, carry the complete authority of Rome. Though you are technically independent of him, a well-placed criticism from his wife could end your career.

"He is one man," Pilate says, "and I have an entire province to consider." And with that, he throws his toga over a shoulder and heads back out to the portico.

"What is truth?" you mumble.

A Loophole?

Things have gone from bad to worse when you return outside. The crowd has nearly doubled, filling the courtyard area. The prisoner now stands on the top of the portico steps, facing His unruly accusers. You half expect them to rush Jesus and kill Him on the spot. Only the fierce presence of the Roman soldiers and the palace guard keeps them from doing so.

Pilate sits in the judgment seat, his hands outstretched, demanding silence. The din of the crowd eventually subsides, though a few derisive voices still ring out. Pilate waits on them, refusing to speak until there is complete silence. You see the sweat glistening on the procurator's brow as he tries to act authoritative, his hands clamped to the arms of his chair. You realize that you are holding your breath.

"I find no grounds for charging this man," Pilate announces.

"No!" screams the high priest. His cry is echoed by a hundred others, all shouting at once, accusing the defendant of every crime imaginable. Pilate seems stunned by their vehemence. He tries to wait them out, but their voices increase in volume and rage. Pilate glances at the walls of the Antonia Fortress. The presence of the soldiers seems to calm him.

The religious leaders eventually quiet the crowd and then start parading witnesses forward, one at a time. Jesus threatened the temple. Jesus urged rebellion against Rome. Jesus said we should not pay taxes. One after another they come, but Jesus just stands there like a statue, never answering their charges. His eyes never leave His accusers, yet He remains surprisingly silent.

Pilate turns to glance at you and then back at the prisoner. You've been through hundreds of trials with the procurator. Together you've seen grown men beg and argue and curse. You've seen them lunge at their attackers. You watched one man clutch his chest and die. But this you've never seen.

Answer them! You want to scream. *Defend yourself!* You expect more from the man who bills Himself as the vaunted Jewish Messiah.

"Are You not answering anything?" Pilate asks. "Look how many things they are accusing You of."

But Jesus doesn't even acknowledge the procurator. Instead, He keeps His eyes glued on His next accuser.

Pilate shakes his head, as if wondering how he can help a man intent on destroying Himself. *Amazing.*

"He stirs up the people," the next witness claims, "teaching throughout all Judea, from Galilee where He started even to here."

It hits you like a lightning bolt from Zeus. *Did he say "Galilee"?* "Your Excellency," you say.

Pilate leans back as you take a few steps forward and whisper in his ear. His Excellency smiles and straightens in his chair. "Are You a Galilean?" Pilate asks Jesus. Lacking an answer, Pilate turns to the witness. "Did you say He was a Galilean?"

The man goes pale, taking a step back toward the mob.

Pilate points a majestic finger eastward. "I find this man to be a Galilean. Our jurisdictional law therefore requires that He first be interrogated by Herod." The crowd begins shouting in protest, but Pilate has made up his mind. He turns to his soldiers. "See that He gets there in one piece."

Though it is still early, Pilate invites you inside for some of his best Galilean wine. "In honor of our prisoner, who is now being examined by my friend Herod." He chortles at the thought. "One madman examining another."

The wine is excellent, but you hardly taste it. For some reason you can't get your mind off the Galilean. "Why wouldn't He defend Himself?" you ask Pilate.

"Because He knew the empire's best assessore would do it for Him." Pilate extends his glass in a toast.

You touch glasses with the procurator, but you don't feel much like celebrating. The law in all its majesty reduced to this? An innocent man at the mercy of a demented ruler. "Do you think Herod will send Him back?" you ask.

"Herod?" Pilate chuckles. "He may send part of Him back. Whether it will be just His head or just His body is anybody's guess."

A DEAL FOR THE DEVIL

An hour later Jesus is back, all of Him, and Pilate is not happy.

The proceedings have been moved to the Stone Pavement—an elevated platform on the other side of the praetorium. Pilate chose this location for its historic grandeur (procurators traditionally delivered speeches here), the larger size of the courtyard surrounding it, and its proximity to the scourging post.

Jesus looks worse than ever. This time you are struck by the contrast between His battered appearance and the elegant purple robe now draped around His shoulders. You have been told that Herod put it on Him and then made sport of the "king of the Jews." If it bothers Jesus, He doesn't show it. His dignity in the face of relentless mocking impresses you most of all.

The crowd has grown to nearly a thousand, and there is a dangerous sense of desperation in the air. The Stone Pavement area reeks of body odor and vitriol. Pilate sits uneasily in his judgment seat, plainly concerned about the growing mob before him. This time he doesn't even address the prisoner.

"You have brought me this man as one who subverts the people," Pilate begins. "But in fact, after examining Him in your presence, I have found no grounds to charge this man with those things you accuse Him of." At this, the mob roars their disapproval. The Roman soldiers take a step toward the crowd, and the noise gradually subsides.

"Neither has Herod," Pilate continues, "because he sent Him back to us. Clearly, He has done nothing to deserve death." The crowd starts to shout him down again, but Pilate raises his voice and continues. "Therefore I will have Him whipped and then release Him."

The crowd objects and surges forward, but the Roman guards raise their shields and force them back. The guards form a wedge around the prisoner, who stands impassively at the foot of the platform as if the proceedings were about someone else entirely.

The scourging will begin in a few minutes, yet Jesus looks right at His accusers, almost as if He feels sorry for them. You think of this man's flesh being torn from His body by the metal talons on the end of the whip. It spurs you into action—a desperate tactic that could cost you dearly.

"Your Excellency." Pilate motions you forward and you kneel next to his chair. "I have an idea." You remind Pilate of the Roman tradition of releasing one prisoner on the day before Passover. "Make them choose between Barabbas and Jesus," you suggest.

Pilate frowns. "Barabbas killed another Jew," he says. "One of his own people. Then he killed a Roman guard during his arrest. I'm not giving up Barabbas."

A skirmish erupts between some members of the crowd and the soldiers. The soldiers rough up a few men on the fringes, and a woman is knocked to the ground. The crowd retreats. Others start yelling, and the crowd surges in a different direction. Shields are raised again, and the soldiers close their flanks. There are shouted accusations.

"You won't have to," you promise. "The Jews all hate Barabbas. I know this to be true."

The procurator is sweating profusely. "Are you sure?"

"Positive."

He nods. Then he stands and waits for the crowd to quiet. "You have a custom that I am to release one prisoner to you at Passover," Pilate says. "Who is it you want me to release for you—Barabbas or Jesus who is called the Messiah?"

Things start happening all at once. The procurator is handed a note. He reads it and swallows visibly, his mouth set in a grave line.

Meanwhile, the priests and elders are huddling among themselves. Then they start working the crowd. They turn back to Pilate just as the procurator hands the note to you. They announce their decision.

"Give us Barabbas!" they cry. You gasp and draw a short breath. *Barabbas!*

You look for Joseph of Arimathea. For other friends you have made through the years among the Jewish people. Where is the voice of reason?

Pilate suddenly seems bolder. He thrusts out his jaw. "Then what should I do with Jesus?"

"Crucify Him!" the priests yell. The crowd takes up the chant: "Crucify Him! Crucify Him!"

There is more pushing in the courtyard. The soldiers move forward and club a few troublemakers. You glance at the note. A message from Claudia, Pilate's wife: "Have nothing to do with that righteous man, for today I've suffered terribly in a dream because of Him."

But you have no time to think about the words. The crowd is clamoring for a crucifixion. The soldiers are losing their patience. You begin to worry for Pilate's safety. He turns to the commander of the battalion. "Deliver Barabbas!" he orders.

The crowd in front cheers first, then a roar of approval ripples across the courtyard. A few minutes later, Barabbas staggers into the sunlight and is greeted like a conquering hero.

Where did things turn so bad?

Pilate steps from the judgment seat and orders a bowl of water. He glances toward his praetorium, undoubtedly checking for Claudia, then dips his hands in the bowl and shakes off the water. It is meant to be an act of bravado, but you notice his hands trembling. For that matter, so are yours. "I am innocent of this man's blood," Pilate says. "See to it yourselves."

"His blood be on us and on our children!"

Pilate shakes his head, fires a reproving look your way, as if to remind you of your bold and flawed prediction, and orders his guards to release Barabbas. Then, his shoulders sagging like those of a beaten man, Pilate issues another order. You want to protest, but you're in no position to argue. The guards salute and lead Jesus away for the flogging.

ONE STRIPE SHORT OF DEATH

Though you're not sure why, you follow Jesus to the whipping post. Perhaps you hope the soldiers will show a little mercy if they know an assessore is watching. But these men, both burly Syrians, seem little impressed with your station in life. Or your nationality. You remember that under a decree of Julius Caesar, no Roman soldier may conduct a scourging, because it is deemed too barbaric.

You're about to be reminded of why.

The gruff Syrians remove the prisoner's expensive robe and slash His undergarments with a knife, removing them as well. They push Him face first against the post and tie His arms high over His head, so Jesus nearly hangs there, every muscle on His back and legs stretched taut. You are no longer surprised when the prisoner offers no resistance, accepting His fate with unsettling calm. You shudder for Him, thinking of what will follow.

The post is in the middle of a small walled-in courtyard, the ground covered with stone slabs stained with blood. Under Roman law, the mob has not been allowed to witness this event.

There are two whips next to the post. One, the *flagellum,* is composed of a wooden handle and a smooth leather strap. The other, the *flagrum,* has pieces of glass and metal attached to the strap. The garrison commander looks at you and smiles spitefully. He gestures toward the flagrum.

The larger of the Syrians grabs the whip and steps back, measuring his distance. The first blow whistles through the air, a blur of brown leather and black metal, but it barely grazes the back of Jesus. "I missed," he says laughingly, then sends another blow whistling through the air, this time grazing the prisoner's legs. You've seen them do this once before, a little game of psychological torture before the real brutality begins. The last time the soldiers did this, the prisoner screamed before the blows ever landed. Jesus, to your amazement, barely flinches.

That changes with the third blow. This time the Syrian swings with all his might, landing the blow squarely on the lower back. The guard jerks the whip back, but the sharp points have dug into the side of Jesus, like a fishing line snagged on a tree limb. The soldier yanks again, and the whip snaps free, pulling a ribbon of flesh and muscle with it.

"One!" shouts the other Syrian gleefully.

You gasp and the whip sails through the air again. Upper back. Lower back. Buttocks. Legs. One even wraps around the face. Five blows. Six. Seven. The blood is pouring from the back of Jesus, His skin flayed open as the guard puts his entire body into the blows, grunting as each one lands. The metal bites into the flesh, blood and sweat spraying from the body of the prisoner. Jesus trembles as He waits for each new blow, then moans as the metal finds its mark, His body jerked to and fro with the force of each blow.

"Was that six or seven?" the man with the whip asks, laughing.

"I'm not sure," says the other, "maybe we should start over."

Your stomach churns and you grit your teeth to hold back the bile. You can no longer watch, diverting your eyes in shame to the ground in front of you.

You want to rescue Jesus, stop this mindless torture, free Him before it's too late. But you have no power here. In fact, your presence seems to infuriate the guards.

You turn to leave, wondering how any man can survive such torture, when the horrible rhythm of the flagrum falls silent. You turn back and watch as the man without the whip walks up to the prisoner and checks on Him. The slightest flicker of hope crawls up your spine. The guard grabs Jesus by the hair and yanks His head to the side, apparently checking for breathing. He rams Jesus's head against the pole, then nods at his companion. The flagrum begins its course anew.

Sickened, you turn and leave the courtyard.

You do not go far. Just outside the wall, you slouch to the ground, listening as the flagrum sings through the air and finds new flesh. You have become disoriented by the violence, the ground spinning beneath you. You count the blows, knowing that few men can survive more than forty minus one. This time, you make no effort to stop the vomit, repulsed by what you've just seen and the role you've played.

At thirty-nine the lashes stop for the final time. You listen for a sound from the prisoner—anything to suggest He's still alive—but you hear only laughter and coarse language from the guards. You stumble back to the entrance of the courtyard, taking pains to stay out of sight so that the Syrians will not be angered again by your presence.

The sight of Jesus makes you want to vomit again. The prisoner is nearly unrecognizable. They have filleted every inch of His back, tearing the skin and muscle to the point where in some spots you can see bone. He is on all fours, clearly in shock, His body shivering even in the heat of the morning sun. One of the conscripts takes a bucket of salt water and sloshes it over Jesus, causing Him to scream in agony. You will later learn that they do that to lessen the bleeding and revive the prisoner for His expected walk to Calvary.

You watch as the Syrians help Him to His feet and then punch Him. They kneel before Jesus and mockingly call Him king of the Jews. One fashions a crown of thorns and jams it on the prisoner's head, causing new rivulets of blood to drip down Jesus's face. They put Herod's robe back on Jesus and kneel again. They shove a branch in His hand as a scepter. Then they take back the branch and pummel Him with it.

They begin prodding the prisoner toward the gate where you are standing in the shadows. You slip out and rush back to the praetorium. For the first time in your life, you are ashamed to be a Roman.

How did it ever come to this? you wonder. *When did things spin so out of control?*

2

WHO CAN FORGIVE SINS BUT GOD?

Three years earlier.

How can a man so cursed be so blessed? the man with the shriveled legs wonders. *What have I ever done to deserve friends like these? How can I ever repay them?*

Four friends, each holding one corner of the paralyzed man's mat, march in unison, sweat dripping from their chins. "I've got to take a quick break," huffs one. They gingerly place the mat down and bend over, hands on knees as they catch their breath. A couple of the men stretch their backs.

Hurry, the paralyzed man thinks, though he doesn't say a word. *Please hurry!*

"Okay," says the smallest of the friends. Without another word, they pick up the mat and resume their journey. Another few hundred yards.

Inside, the house is crowded and the mood is tense. There are Pharisees and teachers of the Law in attendance who have come from villages across Galilee and Judea and from Jerusalem (see Luke 5:17). Though Jesus speaks with conviction, it's clear they're not buying it—a lot of crossed arms and furrowed brows. But He doesn't let up. Jesus talks of a need for repentance and faith, His voice quickening as He discusses the kingdom of God.

The crowd is standing room only. Even the doorway is blocked with those mesmerized by this miracle worker, this prophet who teaches with uncommon authority. Suddenly He stops as some dried mud sprinkles on His listeners. They shuffle back, pushing each other to avoid the debris, while another shower of dried mud and twigs falls. All eyes turn upward. It's obvious that somebody is digging through the roof. "Hey!" somebody shouts. "What're you doing?"

Jesus just smiles.

More debris falls, opening a large hole in the roof, forcing the crowd to surge back to avoid being hit. There are a few more shouts. One or two men from the doorway hustle up the outside steps to see what's going on. When they reach the roof, they make no attempt to stop the interlopers.

The crowd quiets as they realize what's happening. Four men on the roof have tied ropes to the corners of their paralyzed friend's mat. They lower him through the roof as others inside help settle the man softly at the feet of Jesus. The man looks up with expectant and misty eyes, the first sign of hope in many years. Jesus, still smiling, gazes up at the men on the roof, then down at the paralytic. He shakes His head in amazement, impressed by their ingenious faith.

"Friend, your sins are forgiven you," Jesus says (Luke 5:20).

The crowd erupts into spontaneous applause. "Praise God!" says the paralytic. His friends, shouting hallelujahs, pull the paralyzed man back up through the ceiling and prepare for their long journey home. This time the trip will seem to be all downhill, the load lightened by the knowledge that the paralytic is now forgiven. The paralytic feels as if he could float home even without the mat.

The lawyers and Pharisees are awed by the power of God. Oh yeah…and just before the paralyzed man and his entourage leave, they settle up for the damage to the roof.

I know, that's not exactly how it goes. Jesus did more than just deal with the paralyzed man's sins; Jesus also healed him. For that, the paralytic had not just his friends to thank but also the skeptical lawyers and Pharisees. We'll see why in just a moment.

But first, let me ask a critical question: if the story *had* ended without Jesus providing physical healing, how would you feel about it? That Jesus had cheated the paralyzed man? tricked him? mocked him? We all sense that the man and his friends came for physical healing, not just spiritual cleansing. How would this man have felt if Jesus had pronounced forgiveness of sins and then sent him home still paralyzed?

It's academic, you say. Jesus knew the Pharisees would object to His statement about forgiving the man's sins and that this would provide an opportunity for healing. In other words, Jesus knew all along that He would provide healing for this man.

Maybe. But what about the thousands of others whom Jesus didn't heal while He walked the earth? What about the millions since then who have begged Christ for healing from cancer or paralysis or some other debilitating disorder, only to have the heavens remain silent?

We can explain this away with any number of platitudes or high-minded philosophies, but at the end of the day, we must get comfortable with an unyielding truth: Jesus will always answer our prayers for forgiveness, but He doesn't always answer our prayers for healing. At least not the way we want them answered.

Sometimes He does what He did on that magical day in Capernaum when the paralytic was literally dropped into His lap. But even then Jesus made it clear that His first priority was the spiritual condition of this man, not his physical condition.

> Seeing their faith He said, "Friend, your sins are forgiven you."
>
> Then the scribes[1] and Pharisees began to reason: "Who is this man who speaks blasphemies? Who can forgive sins but God alone?"
>
> But perceiving their thoughts, Jesus replied to them, "Why are you reasoning this in your hearts? Which is easier: to say, 'Your sins are forgiven you,' or to say, 'Get up and walk'? But so you may know that the Son of Man has authority on earth to forgive sins"—He told the paralyzed man, "I tell you: get up, pick up your [mat], and go home."
>
> Immediately he got up before them, picked up what he had been lying on, and went home glorifying God. Then everyone was astounded, and they were giving glory to God. And they were filled with awe and said, "We have seen incredible things today!" (Luke 5:20–26)

COSMIC TURF

Can you imagine the looks on the faces of the scribes and Pharisees? First, Jesus read their minds, then He destroyed their arguments with a miraculous healing. It's a stretch to even call this encounter a cross-examination of Christ. If anything, He cross-examined His adversaries while they sat in silence, dumbfounded by a prophet who could divine their thoughts. How would you like to be on the witness stand facing a lawyer who says, "I know what you're thinking"…and then demonstrates that he does?

But I include this episode because it's Christ's first encounter with His critics and it sets the stage for the hostilities that follow. The central conflict is defined: Christ claims to be more than a prophet. He puts Himself on equal footing with God by forgiving sins. In their hearts, the lawyers and Pharisees are thinking, *Who can forgive sins but God?* Christ doesn't argue with their premise. Instead, He demonstrates that He has such authority. To the Pharisees, this is blasphemy (see Mark 2:7).

From the very beginning, Jesus leaves no middle ground. By claiming the power to forgive sins, He stakes out some cosmic turf where mortals cannot trespass. People must either receive Him as God, as the paralytic did, or reject Him as a fraud, as the Pharisees and lawyers did. In *Mere Christianity,* a powerful primer on the fundamentals of the faith, C. S. Lewis describes it this way:

A man who was merely a man and said the sort of things Jesus said would not be a great moral teacher. He would either be a lunatic—on a level with the man who says he is a poached egg—or else he would be the Devil of Hell. You must make your choice. Either this man was, and is, the Son of God: or else a madman or something worse.[2]

For the Pharisees and lawyers, Jesus was "something worse." They may have been silenced on this day—stunned by this mind reader from Nazareth—but they would be back. And, as we will see, they would spend the next three years doing everything possible to undermine Christ's ministry.

But if we're not careful here, we'll overlook a critical aspect of this story. We'll put the spotlight on the miraculous healing of this paralyzed man, or even on the budding conflict between Christ and the Pharisees, and we'll miss what this story reveals about the priorities of Jesus. He cared more about this man's spiritual condition than He did about the man's physical condition. Jesus dealt with the paralyzed man's sins first—and might not have healed the man at all if the lawyers and Pharisees hadn't been there.

The healing was almost an afterthought. "Okay, just so you'll know I really can forgive sins—watch this!" But I wonder if the crowd would have gone away praising God if the healing had not occurred. I wonder the same thing about the paralytic and his friends.

ARE HIS PRIORITIES OURS?

Many in today's churches would reverse the priorities of Christ. "Get up and walk" becomes the main thing; "your sins are forgiven" is an afterthought.

Do you disagree? Go with me to two typical church meetings (one on each end of the evangelical Christian spectrum), and I'll show you what I mean.

The first takes place in a large coliseum. It could be anywhere, but we'll put this one in Madison Square Garden. The preacher is a well-known television evangelist with a comb-over that defies the laws of nature. If he can get that hair to stay in place, healing should be a piece of cake.

We take our seats in the back row of the top section and enjoy the praise and worship. Despite ourselves, we even enjoy the preaching, drawn in by the captivating personality of the man on stage. Then comes the climax of the service: an altar call in which miracles of healing are performed. People flood the altar, some in wheelchairs, others with canes, many with hidden ailments—cancer, blood disorders, heart disease. Bad backs are a dime a dozen. The altar gets so crowded that we half expect someone to be lowered onto the stage, like the paralytic in our story, just to get the attention of the evangelist.

Emotions reach a fever pitch as trophies of healing are paraded across the stage. This crippled brother now walks. That deaf sister now hears. They fall over backward as the evangelist slays them in the Spirit. The crowd claps its approval.

Strangely, nobody comes on stage to announce "only" a change in his or her spiritual condition. This crowd wants miracles, not just repentance. Sure, they know Jesus can heal us spiritually, but what about our bodies? He wants to heal us physically, too.

Right about now, you might be ready to put this book down, or even throw it at me, infuriated by my description of what goes on in these faith-healing meetings. Maybe you've been there. Maybe you've been healed there.

Don't get me wrong. I'm not saying that Christ doesn't heal today. His miraculous power in our time is just as strong as it was when He walked the earth. Maybe even stronger. After all, Jesus promised that those who believed in Him would do "greater works" than Jesus did "because I am going to the Father" (John 14:12). To say that Jesus doesn't answer prayers for healing today would be to call Him a liar.

But I am saying that Jesus doesn't *owe* us physical healing. He's not obligated to heal all of our ailments anytime we utter the magic prayer words. And I'm also saying that the spiritual, not the physical, should be our primary concern.

But if you're still upset about my description of the faith-healing meetings, hang in there for a few more paragraphs. We're about to head over to the other side of town.

We leave Madison Square Garden and hop in a cab, taking us to the Connecticut suburbs. We find a brick church with a tall steeple at a prominent intersection. We've arrived just in time for the Wednesday-night prayer meeting.

We try to slip into a back pew, but they're already taken. Not to worry. It's prayer meeting night, so there are lots of empty seats. We grab a pew halfway up, near the aisle.

After a thirty-minute sermon, the pastor has just started taking prayer requests. *Aunt Alma had a stroke but is recovering. Pray for full use of her right arm... My neighbor's husband just went in for a biopsy— pray the mass will be benign; they've got three small kids...* That reminds somebody, *Did you see that article in the paper about that little eight-year-old boy with brain cancer?* There are sympathy moans and nods. *We need to pray for him... We're going on family vacation to Virginia and need traveling mercies... Joe's job, don't forget Joe's job.* And so it goes. At the end of the request time, there is a long list of organ problems and cancer cases. Somebody might mention an unsaved friend or relative. Somebody else mentions the missionaries. Of course we need to pray for them, even the healthy ones. Nobody gets healed in these meetings, but the focus is still on the physical and material needs, not on the spiritual ones.

There is, of course, nothing wrong with heartfelt prayers for our physical needs. Does Jesus care about those needs? You bet. He healed hundreds, maybe thousands. Even the hairs on our head are all numbered (see Matthew 10:30). Every physical challenge we face has been filtered by God. He uses our weaknesses to glorify Him and to help us grow in grace. But He doesn't want us to focus *primarily* on the physical needs of this world. Even the Pharisees believed in the resurrection of the dead; they just didn't live in light of eternity.

If we're not careful, we will fall into the same trap. Sure, we believe in heaven. And we want to live eternally with Jesus someday. But, to be honest, most of us don't want that day to come anytime soon—not for us and not for our loved ones. We want a long life here, in this world. And a healthy one. And a prosperous one. "To live is Christ and to die is gain," said the apostle Paul (Philippians 1:21, NIV). But sometimes we modify that a little. To live is Christ, and to live better and longer, that's real gain.

"Where your treasure is, there your heart will be also," Jesus warned (Matthew 6:21, NIV). But how do we pray? Bless our business. Help us get this house or that car or this raise or that promotion. Basically, help us heap up treasures on earth.

Heal our bodies. Fill our wallets. Increase our fame. And while you're at it, if you've still got a minute or two, forgive us our sins.

SAM BROWN AND THE CHOCOLATE POWERBAR

"Your marathon clock is ticking," Sam said to a thirty-five-year-old Randy Singer. "If you're ever going to do one of these things, you'd better do it now, before your body falls completely apart."

Sam, a friend and orthopedic surgeon, was training for the Marine Corps Marathon. He challenged me to join him. "You may be too old already," Sam said, looking me up and down. "Maybe you should just stick to 10Ks."

I started training immediately. Sam and I decided to do some practice runs together, but we soon found that our approaches were very different. Sam believed in following a disciplined training schedule; I believed that determination and guts could make up for the few hundred miles of training I'd skipped. Sam charted the course, learned where all the water stops were, and developed a strategy for the race. My strategy was simple: left foot, right foot, left foot, right foot...follow the guys in front of me.

In one of my favorite scriptural analogies, the apostle Paul says that the Christian life is like a race. "Run in such a way that you may win," he urges (1 Corinthians 9:24). The writer of Hebrews picks up on this same imagery, urging us to "run with endurance the race that lies before us, keeping our eyes on Jesus, the source and perfecter of our faith" (Hebrews 12:1–2). The thoughts are the same: focus on the finish line; run strong.

My lack of training really caught up to me in the last few miles, but overall I had an average race. Since I'm an average runner, that was fine with me. In fact, I'm so average that you can basically set the curve by me. Out of eighteen thousand runners that year, I finished at spot nine thousand. On the nose. Mr. Average.

Sam's race was far more interesting. We ended up getting separated early in the race. But Sam is a likable guy who could carry on a conversation with anyone, so he made a new friend and chatted with this guy for several miles, even stopping once to pose for pictures. Eventually, Sam got separated from his new friend and ran mostly on his own.

His mind started playing tricks on him, and his body craved nutrition. By mile seventeen, Sam was focused on one thing and one thing only: PowerBars.

Because of his careful prerace planning, Sam knew there was a PowerBar station at mile nineteen. Sam let his mind drift to that station about two miles before he got there. He'd already enjoyed the water and Gatorade stations, but this was the first and only PowerBar stop. His body needed a chocolate PowerBar. Yearned for a chocolate PowerBar. It would help him get through that last seven miles. It would carry him over the famous wall that marathoners hit. A Power-Bar. Sweet, sweet PowerBar. He thought about little else for two miles.

Imagine Sam's dismay when he finally made it to mile-marker nineteen only to discover that the chocolate PowerBars were gone! In fact, all the PowerBars were gone. Surrounding the table where they had been neatly stacked just a few thousand runners earlier were scraps of PowerBar wrappers, scattered among the discarded water cups and trampled underfoot by runners. As Sam would tell me later, just the sight of it made him feel like quitting. The ever-efficient marines had underestimated the number of PowerBars they needed. How could anyone finish the last seven miles without one?

"I don't know what came over me," Sam later explained, "but I was just obsessed with those PowerBars. I squatted down and started picking up PowerBar wrappers that had little scraps left in them, like a homeless person looking for dinner. After a few mostly empty wrappers, I suddenly realized how ridiculous this all was. I got up, looked around to make sure nobody was watching, then finished the race."

When Sam told me this story after the race, I couldn't help laughing. Think about it—a few more miles and Sam would have been at the finish line, enjoying all the PowerBars and bananas he could eat, all the Gatorade he could drink. Instead, my distinguished friend, a disciplined and spirited runner, became so distracted at mile nineteen that he found himself scrounging around on the ground, searching through empty PowerBar wrappers.

Sometimes in today's church we end up doing the same thing. We are in a spiritual race, running for the prize of the high calling of God in Christ Jesus. The Son of God stands at the finish line urging us on, telling us to keep our focus on Him. There are heavenly crowns to be won. A banquet to be enjoyed. An eternity to spend with our friends, our family, and our Savior.

But in the meantime there's a race to be won. "Let us lay aside every weight and the sin that so easily ensnares us, and run with endurance the race that lies before us" (Hebrews 12:1). Get rid of that baggage! Keep moving. Left foot, right foot, left foot, right foot.

And where are we? Scrounging around for scraps of chocolate PowerBars, licking the wrappers clean. But we need this in order to finish the race, we reason. We need healing to better serve the Lord. More money to give to His causes. More years to lead others into the kingdom.

All of that may be true, but if we focus too much on the things we need in this world, we lose sight of what matters in the next. "Seek first the kingdom of God and His righteousness, and all these things will be provided for you" (Matthew 6:33).

PowerBars or finish line? Luxury or sacrifice? The praise of people or the commendation of Christ? These are the choices we make every day.

Our life is a "bit of smoke," says James the brother of Christ (James 4:14). Here today, gone tomorrow. The finish line will be here quicker than we think. Our duty is to keep our eyes fixed on Jesus.

JUST THE PRESIDENT?

This is a lofty goal—living in light of eternity, putting the kingdom of God first. But what does that mean as a practical matter? The story of Jesus at the house in Capernaum is a useful illustration, but it's not like we go around forgiving sins and healing people. In the twenty-first century, how do we keep our focus away from the PowerBar wrappers and on the marathon course?

At the memorial service for Dr. Bill Bright, the prolific soul winner and founder of Campus Crusade for Christ, my friend Bob Reccord shared about his last meeting with Dr. Bright. At the time of Bob's visit, Dr. Bright already had an advanced case of pulmonary fibrosis and could breathe only with great difficulty.

"I know it must be painful," Bob said. "I'm sorry."

Dr. Bright smiled and shook his head. "Compared to what my Jesus went through on the cross," he wheezed, "this is nothing. Really."

They talked for a while before their conversation was interrupted by a phone call. Bob gave Dr. Bright a chance to speak to the caller in private.

A few minutes later Vonette (Dr. Bright's wife) led Bob back into the room. She turned to Dr. Bright. "Tell Bob who that was," she suggested.

"No," Dr. Bright responded. "It's not that important."

But Vonette and Bob were relentless, and Dr. Bright finally gave in. "It was the president," he said.

"The *president?*" said Bob. "As in *the* President of the United States?"

"Yes," Dr. Bright said. "President Bush just wanted to check on me and let me know that he is praying for me."

Bob was floored. Both by the thoughtfulness of the president and the nonchalance of Dr. Bright. "What an incredible honor," Bob gushed. "You must have been blown away."

"It was nice," said Dr. Bright. *Nice?!* "But frankly, when you're getting ready to meet the Savior of the universe face to face, even a call from the president pales in comparison."

PASSION AND PURPOSE

Living for eternity—what does that really mean? For one thing, it means we have no fear of dying. But for another, it means we live like this world is not our home. We don't just face death differently; we handle life differently, putting an emphasis on the spiritual, not the physical. We finish strong, like Dr. Bright. And we run strong in the meantime. It means that we don't spend our days just trying to prolong them; we don't just exist—we live with passion.

Noted American novelist Jack London *(White Fang, Call of the Wild)*, eloquently captured this thought: "I would rather be ashes than dust! I would rather that my spark should burn out in a brilliant blaze than it should be stifled by dry-rot.... The function of man is to live, not to exist. I shall not waste my days in trying to prolong them. I shall use my time."[3]

But London's passion was misplaced. At age forty the famous novelist died. Massive debts, alcoholism, and a paranoid fear of losing his creativity darkened his final days. It is still debated whether he died from a gastrointestinal infection or from suicide by morphine. The point? Running the race hard is not enough. If our focus is not on Jesus, our passion will have no purpose.

Which takes us back to that crowded house in Capernaum.

Doesn't it seem to you that Jesus was unnecessarily antagonistic that day? He had to know that the lawyers and Pharisees would become resolute and powerful enemies if He didn't treat them with a little respect. And nothing would rile them more than Jesus's claiming that He had the ability to forgive sins. How could they not interpret this as blasphemy?

What's more, the lawyers and Pharisees didn't even *say* anything. It's almost as if Jesus were aching for a fight. He read their thoughts and then castigated them in front of dozens of witnesses for words they had never verbalized. He embarrassed them. He called them out. This is a far cry from the soft and cuddly Jesus we hear so much about (usually from folks who ignore biblical stories like this one).

Didn't Jesus know that He was sealing His own fate? He was supposed to be omnipotent—or at least a great prophet. It doesn't take a prophet to know that when you alienate groups as powerful as these religious leaders—a whole house full of them, in this case—you risk exactly the kind of thing that eventually happened to Christ. Either Jesus would have to back down, or these leaders would have to find a way to take Him out. Why couldn't He see that?

Or maybe He did. Maybe He knew exactly what He was doing. Maybe He knew precisely what it would take to secure our salvation —earthly rejection, physical suffering, abandonment by His heavenly Father. Earthly comforts had no allure for Him. The PowerBars at mile nineteen couldn't keep Him from His goal. Maybe He had His eyes on the Cross all along.

His prerogative and His priority were the forgiveness of sins. As God, He had the authority to forgive. But as the Son of God, He knew that authority commanded a terrible price. He would make some powerful enemies and suffer a humiliating death. But when He saw the paralyzed man leap for joy, He knew it would be worth it.

On this day He passed a point of no return with the Pharisees. This was Christ's Rubicon. The humiliated lawyers and Pharisees couldn't back down now, and neither would He. Either Jesus was God or He was not. Left foot, right foot, left foot, right foot. He had begun His inexorable march toward the Cross. Nothing could stop Him.

Luke would later describe it this way: "He set His face like flint toward Jerusalem" (see Luke 9:51, KJV).

46

3

BLOODY BAND-AIDS
AND TELLTALE HEARTS

It was my last trial before I left the private practice of law to become the general counsel for the North American Mission Board. I wanted it to be something special, something I would be proud to tell others about, something memorable. I wanted to go out with a bang.

Well, one out of four is not bad. It was definitely memorable.

I ended up trying the case at the last minute. One of my partners had done a good job of pretrial preparation but was sick of the case and didn't want to take it to trial. (In a minute, you'll see why.) He knew I liked trying cases. And sure enough, I bit.

Our client was a fast-food restaurant being sued by a customer. It seems that this customer had ordered a cheeseburger at the drive-through and ended up with some extra protein. One of the workers had earlier cut his finger and put some Band-Aids on the cut to stop the bleeding. There were three small Band-Aids in all.

According to the pretrial testimony of the customer, he found these Band-Aids while eating his cheeseburger in the parking lot of the fast-food restaurant. After biting into the cheeseburger—*Mmm, this texture isn't quite right*—he got nauseated and eventually found a lawyer. He testified that he discovered two small Band-Aids between the burger and bun, leaving a slight mystery about the third one. Meanwhile, my client's employee was wondering where those Band-Aids had gone, since they had apparently slipped off his finger.

"Interesting," I said when my partner first described the case to me. "It doesn't sound like we have much of a defense."

He smiled as he passed me the file. "Looks like you've got a good handle on it."

I had a habit of practicing my opening statement with my wife the night before a trial. It usually gave me a pretty good feel as to how a jury might react. I told her the facts of the case and launched into a vigorous defense of my embattled client. When I finished thirty minutes later, she had one word for me. "Settle."

"We tried. My client made a reasonable offer to open settlement negotiations, but then the plaintiff came back asking for a settlement well into six figures. It was so high we didn't even respond."

"Settle," she repeated.

But then I told her one additional fact—my secret weapon.

"Hmm," she said. "That would make things interesting."

We didn't settle. The next morning, I found myself in court facing the real jury. Before we started our opening statements, the judge asked if we were trying to settle the case.

"They're not offering any real money," the plaintiff's lawyer said.

"We made a reasonable offer," I countered.

The judge sighed.

The plaintiff's attorney gave his opening statement first. He detailed his client's horrible day at our fast-food restaurant. He talked about all the evidence that tied the bloody Band-Aids to our employee. He accused us of gross negligence (imagine that).

Then he launched into a litany of problems that this incident had caused the plaintiff. Nausea and sickness (hey, we offered him another cheeseburger). Fear of AIDS (though he had tested negative for HIV, the disease has a long incubation period and therefore the tests were not yet conclusive). He couldn't sleep at night. His job performance as a firefighter was affected by the experience. His girlfriend broke up with him. As I listened, my wife's advice was ringing in my head.

When it was my turn to deliver my opening, I went right to the damages issue. Seems like a lot of trauma from a few bloody Band-Aids, I said. Then I pulled out a deposition transcript from another case—one that the plaintiff had filed in the Norfolk court system, just a few miles up the road from this Virginia Beach courthouse. It was a case that even his attorney in the bloody Band-Aid case didn't know about.

"At the same time that the plaintiff is marching into this courtroom and claiming that these two bloody Band-Aids caused all this turmoil in his life, he's also giving testimony in another court up the road in Norfolk, Virginia, saying these exact same problems were caused by a traffic accident, where somebody hit him from behind at a red light."

I proceeded to describe the pretrial discovery process, in which litigants are required to give sworn deposition testimony, and then began reading from the plaintiff's deposition in the traffic-accident case. It contained a nearly word-for-word list of the complaints his attorney had just listed in his opening statement, except in the deposition from the other case the plaintiff blamed them on a bad back resulting from the traffic accident. He testified about sickness, loss of sleep, job performance, and even breaking up with his girlfriend—it was all there, everything except the fear of AIDS.

Jury members began crossing their arms and shooting skeptical glances at the plaintiff. After my opening, the judge called us up to his bench and addressed the plaintiff's attorney. "Has Mr. Singer offered you anything in settlement?" the judge asked.

"Not really," said the plaintiff's lawyer. "Just a ridiculously low amount."

"You'd better take whatever he's offering," said the judge.

We settled less than an hour later. In the parking lot one of the jurors stopped me. "Hope you didn't pay him much," the juror said.

"The amount is confidential," I replied, "but I think it was fair."

"We weren't going to give him a nickel," said the juror.

This shocked me. After all, the man had bitten into at least two bloody Band-Aids.

"Do you mind me asking why? I mean, he *did* find some bloody Band-Aids on his burger."

"Yeah, but we watched him drink out of the same water glass that the paralegal drank from. Nobody with a fear of AIDS would do that. Plus, the testimony from that other case…"

I reached into my suit-coat pocket and felt the clean Band-Aids I had used during my opening to show the jury the approximate size of the ones in question. I left them there for a long time afterward. Every time I put my hand in my suit-coat pocket, they reminded me of two things. First, the importance of integrity. Juries hate anything they perceive as hypocritical or gaming the system. Even a good case can be sabotaged by a lack of integrity. Second, the importance of keeping things in perspective. A trial is supposed to be a search for truth. Juries instinctively understand this. When you lose sight of the real purpose of the law and try to use it for your own advantage, bad things happen.

Guard your integrity and don't lose sight of the spirit of the law. The bloody Band-Aids were the object lesson that drove these points home to me. Christ used a shriveled hand.

LAW AND GRACE

Christ clashed with His critics for one reason above all others: they believed in law; He believed in grace. They obsessed over the letter of the Law; He understood its purpose. For the religious leaders, particularly the Pharisees, religion was a set of rules—do this, don't do that, earn your brownie points with God. Not just rules, mind you, but highly detailed rules, derived in large part from Old Testament writings and administered by—you guessed it—the Pharisees. And they wanted everyone to know how seriously they took these rules.

The Pharisees traced their history back to the second century BC, when the Hebrew Hasidim ("pious ones") opposed the introduction of Greek elements into Jewish culture. By the time of Christ, they were a highly respected and zealous association of men known for their fanatical love of Scripture and the oral tradition of the Mosaic Law. They viewed themselves as purists and separatists, the only ones in Israel serious about keeping the Law.

To demonstrate their seriousness, they created hedges around the Law—extra rules to keep them from even getting close to violating the Law. They developed more than two thousand hedges and, forgetting that the hedges were creations of people, not God, treated them as equivalent to the Law itself. For example, if the Law said something had to be done by morning, the Pharisees would say it had to be done by midnight the previous night. Since the Law said no work should be done on the Sabbath, the Pharisees put in place hundreds of detailed hedges to keep that from happening. A tailor could not leave a needle in his clothes on Friday afternoon or he might accidentally carry it with him on Saturday and violate the Sabbath command.

To show how pious they were, the Pharisees dressed the part. Blue robes, because the sky was blue, and the color would therefore show they were closer to God.[1] (And you thought North Carolina fans made that up.) They wore a phylactery—a small box that contained a verse of Scripture—on their foreheads. They wore prayer shawls with long tassels. Why? Because God said that when the Israelites saw their tassels move, they would be reminded to obey the commands of the Lord rather than follow their own desires (see Numbers 15:38–40). The Pharisees wore long tassels to symbolize that they remembered better than anyone.

When the Pharisees prayed, they would lift up their voices to heaven, praying loud and long. They would fast for two days each week, looking ragged and weary, emphasizing how much they were suffering. When they gave, they would blow trumpets so the whole world would know how much they plunked into the offering. If the hour of prayer came when they were crossing the street, they would stop and pray right in the middle of the road, making others walk around them.

Everything about them said, "Look at me. I am holy."

Then along came Jesus.

It was inevitable they would clash. Jesus hung out with tax collectors and sinners. The Pharisees were separatists; they hung out only with one another. Jesus was all about the spirit of the Law—why did God give us these commands in the first place? The Pharisees were all about the hedges.

The battle could have been joined on any one of the two thousand or so man-made hedges. It just happened to start with the hedges surrounding fasting and the Sabbath:

People came and asked [Jesus], "Why do John's disciples and
the Pharisees' disciples fast, but Your disciples do not fast?"

Jesus said to them, "The wedding guests cannot fast while
the groom is with them, can they? As long as they have the
groom with them, they cannot fast. But the time will come
when the groom is taken away from them, and then they will
fast in that day."...

On the Sabbath He was going through the grainfields,
and His disciples began to make their way picking some heads
of grain. The Pharisees said to Him, "Look, why are they
doing what is not lawful on the Sabbath?"

He said to them, "Have you never read what David
and those who were with him did when he was in need and
hungry—how he entered the house of God in the time of
Abiathar the high priest and ate the sacred bread—which is
not lawful for anyone to eat except the priests?...

The Sabbath was made for man and not man for the

Sabbath. Therefore the Son of Man is Lord even of the Sabbath." (Mark 2:18–20, 23–28)

Now [Jesus] entered the synagogue again, and a man was there who had a paralyzed hand. In order to accuse Him, they were watching Him closely to see whether He would heal him on the Sabbath. He told the man with the paralyzed hand, "Stand before us." Then He said to them, "Is it lawful on the Sabbath to do good or to do evil, to save life or to kill?" But they were silent. After looking around at them with anger and sorrow at the hardness of their hearts, He told the man, "Stretch out your hand." So he stretched it out, and his hand was restored. Immediately the Pharisees went out and started plotting with the Herodians against Him, how they might destroy Him. (Mark 3:1–6)

As in the Band-Aid case, the Pharisees caught Christ red-handed (pardon the pun). And, like that case, they cared more about using the Law for their own purposes than they did about the object of the Law. Jesus addressed the issue head-on.

It's not about rules; it's about the reason for the rules. The Sabbath was made for man, not man for the Sabbath. As far as fasting is concerned, we fast in order to draw closer to God. Why would we fast when God is here walking among us?

We'll look more at this theme—the spirit of the Law brings life, but the letter of the Law condemns—a little later. But first, let's be equally clear about what Christ *didn't* say in this exchange. This was not a condemnation of the Law. "Don't assume that I came to destroy the Law or the Prophets. I did not come to destroy but to fulfill" (Matthew 5:17). He did not nullify fasting or say we should ignore the Sabbath. On the contrary, He promised that one day His disciples would fast, and He defended the underlying reason for the Sabbath. He just didn't buy into the nitpicky and self-righteous way the religious establishment regulated these spiritual disciplines.

Of course, you say. That's obvious.

If so, then why do some in the church today act as if Christ really said, "Who needs to fast?" and "Sabbath? What Sabbath?"

Satan has enticed us into a dangerous about-face on these issues. Tapping into our proper desire to avoid the self-righteous legalism of the Pharisees, Satan tries to make us ignore fasting and Sabbath observing altogether. When is the last time you heard a sermon about fasting? Or about the purpose and practice of Sabbath rest? Better yet, when is the last time you fasted? How are you doing at honoring God by keeping the Sabbath?

Before we dig deeper into the conflict between Jesus and the Pharisees, let's take a look at these two spiritual disciplines. We will try to consider them, not like the Pharisees did, as if they could earn God's favor by piling up fasting and Sabbath points, but the way Jesus did, using these disciplines to refresh our bodies and draw closer to God.

BUT WHEN YOU FAST...

In Christ's time, fasting was widespread. The Pharisees did it twice a week like clockwork. Other religious leaders did it too. It implied holiness, self-sacrifice, and spiritual intensity. Today it implies that we need to lose a few pounds before some big event.

Christ went on a forty-day fast at the start of His ministry. He predicted that His disciples would fast when He, the Bridegroom, was taken away. (Hey, that would refer to us now!) He gave instructions on how to fast.

Those instructions, contained in the Sermon on the Mount, assume that we *will* fast. "*Whenever* you fast," Christ said, "don't be sad-faced like the hypocrites" (Matthew 6:16, emphasis added). That's the same language He used in the same sermon to talk about giving and praying. "Whenever you give to the poor, don't sound a trumpet before you.... Whenever you pray, you must not be like the hypocrites, because they love to pray standing in the synagogues and on the street corners to be seen by people" (Matthew 6:2, 5).

In other words, it is assumed that we will fast, give, and pray. Jesus just wanted to make sure that we would do these things with a proper motive. Not only that, but Jesus also promised that God would reward those who fast with the right motives and a pure heart:

Whenever you fast, don't be sad-faced like the hypocrites. For they make their faces unattractive so their fasting is obvious to people. I assure you: They've got their reward! But when you fast, put oil on your head, and wash your face, so that you don't show your fasting to people but to your Father who is in secret. And your Father who sees in secret will reward you. (Matthew 6:16–18)

Though the Pharisees distorted the reasons for fasting, Jesus never said that fasting was wrong. Men and women of faith have long fasted in order to grow closer to God, to gain a sense of direction, or to slay the desires of the flesh. Richard Foster, in *Celebration of Discipline*, reminds us that "the list of biblical personages who fasted reads like a 'Who's Who' of Scripture: Moses the lawgiver, David the king, Elijah the prophet, Esther the queen, Daniel the seer, Anna the prophetess, Paul the apostle, Jesus Christ the incarnate Son."[2] The list of Christians throughout church history who fasted is also impressive: Martin Luther, John Calvin, John Knox, John Wesley, Jonathan Edwards, and Charles Finney.[3]

But today fasting has by and large fallen out of favor with the church. After all, it cuts radically against our self-indulgent, instant-gratification, supersize-it culture. Jesus and His disciples went against the peer pressure in their day by refusing to fast. Could it be that today, with the Bridegroom gone, Jesus is calling us to go against the peer pressure in our culture by honoring the discipline of fasting?

Of course, if we fast for the wrong reasons, we might lose a few pounds but make ourselves miserable in the process. A true fast is done for spiritual reasons that focus on self-denial and seeking God. Listen to the benefits of fasting described by Donald Whitney:

> There's something about fasting that sharpens the edge of our intercessions and gives passion to our supplications. So it has frequently been used by the people of God when there is a special urgency about the concerns they lift before the Father....
>
> The Bible does not teach that fasting is a kind of spiritual hunger strike that compels God to do our bidding. If we ask for something outside of God's will, fasting does not cause Him to reconsider. Fasting does not change God's hearing so much as it changes our praying....

Fasting is one of the best friends we can introduce to our prayer life.[4]

Later in His ministry, Jesus would affirm the notion that fasting provides jet fuel to our prayer life. The disciples of Christ tried to cast a demon out of a boy afflicted with seizures, but they failed. After Christ exorcised the demon, "the disciples approached Jesus privately and said, 'Why couldn't we drive it out?' 'Because of your little faith,' He told them.... 'However, this kind does not come out except by prayer and fasting'" (Matthew 17:19–21).

Unlike the Pharisees, Jesus nowhere prescribed the length or frequency of our fasts. Throughout Scripture there are examples of all kinds of fasts, though the most common involves abstinence from food but not drink.[5] Fasts can be as short as one day or as long as forty. We should not focus on the length but on the purpose.

Before leaving the subject, allow me to share some practical advice from Richard Foster concerning extended fasts. I will preface it with the type of disclaimer you might expect from a lawyer like me: check with your physician before attempting any extended fast. It would be wise to fast for shorter periods of time before embarking on a forty-day fast. That said, listen to the way Foster describes an extended fast:

> The first three days are usually the most difficult in terms of physical discomfort and hunger pains. The body is beginning to rid itself of the toxins that have built up over years of poor eating habits, and it is not a comfortable process....

By the fourth day the hunger pains are beginning to sub-side though you will have feelings of weakness and occasional dizziness. The dizziness is only temporary and caused by sudden changes in position.... The weakness can come to the point where the simplest task takes great effort. Rest is the best remedy. Many find this the most difficult period of the fast.

By the sixth or seventh day you will begin to feel stronger and more alert. Hunger pains will continue to diminish until by the ninth or tenth day they are only a minor irritation. The body will have eliminated the bulk of toxins and you will feel good. Your sense of concentration will be sharpened and you will feel as if you could continue fasting indefinitely....

Anywhere between twenty-one and forty days or longer, depending on the individual, hunger pains will return. This is...[a] signal that the body has used up its reserves and is beginning to draw on the living tissue. The fast should be broken at this time.[6]

THE SABBATH WAS MADE FOR MAN

Like fasting, observance of the Sabbath has fallen out of favor in our culture. Blue laws requiring businesses to close on Sunday are long gone. Few retail businesses or restaurants voluntarily close. Our modern workweek, without boundary lines between work and private time, leaves little margin for a day of rest. PDAs, telecommuting, and home offices blur the lines between work and home. Sunday is prime time for athletes from Little League to the majors. Is this what Jesus meant when He said, "The Sabbath was made for man and not man for the Sabbath"?

The subject of Sabbath-day rest in a post-Resurrection world has generated volumes of intense doctrinal debate. Much of that debate hinges on the six separate confrontations between Jesus and the Pharisees.[7] Did Jesus abolish the Sabbath? Did He relegate it to the sphere of ceremonial laws that no longer apply to those who have freedom through Christ? Or was He restoring the true purpose of the Sabbath as a day of restoration and worship rather than a day burdened by man-made rules?

Reasonable minds differ on the nuances, but a few clear principles emerge. First, the concept of Sabbath existed prior to the giving of the Ten Commandments and will still have validity when Christ returns to earth to establish the millennial kingdom. In the first two chapters of Scripture, God set the Sabbath example, creating the world in six days and resting on the seventh. He created us with a need both to rest and to set aside special time to focus on Him. Old Testament passages refer to the Sabbath significantly prior to the Ten Commandments[8] as do prophesies that look past the Second Coming of Christ to the promised Millennium.[9]

Second, just because Christians do not live under the Law does not mean that Sabbath rest is unnecessary. Jesus never disavowed the concept of the Sabbath. For example, in defending the conduct of His disciples when they picked grain on the Sabbath, Jesus used the example of King David and the sacred showbread. Like a good lawyer, Jesus was using precedent to defend His disciples. But it was the precedent of King David, a man plainly under the full authority of the

Mosaic Law. Rather than making a case that the Sabbath no longer applied, Jesus argued that His disciples, like King David, had perfectly complied with the spirit of Sabbath observance under the Law, while ignoring the man-made traditions grafted on by the Pharisees.

In other words, the Pharisees had taken a law instituted for the benefit of man and turned it on its head. They weighed men down with the legalistic burdens of Sabbath-day observance, piling on rules and regulations in the name of piety. But Jesus argued for the original intent of the Sabbath as a day of freedom, joy, rest, and worship. "The Sabbath was made for man and not man for the Sabbath" (Mark 2:27).

Jesus made it clear that the issue isn't whether you pick grain on the Sabbath to eat, heal a paralyzed hand, or even have a needle in a garment that you carry around with you. The issue is whether you set aside one day a week to honor God and restore your strength. For someone like me, the Sabbath can be a day to exercise—to clear my mind from all the clutter of the week and rejuvenate my body. For someone with a job requiring hard physical labor, the Sabbath can be a day to rest and just veg out. For both, the Sabbath is a day of worship.[10]

"Remember the reason for the Sabbath," Jesus is saying. "Don't pervert this holy day by refusing to help a man with a paralyzed hand. I care more about people than about your hedges. The spirit of the Law restores; the letter of the Law destroys." "So [the man with the paralyzed hand] stretched it out, and his hand was restored. Immediately the Pharisees went out and started plotting with the Herodians against Him, how they might destroy Him" (Mark 3:5–6).

THE HEART OF THE MATTER

It was a routine checkup at the Cooper Heart Clinic, something I would do every other year. I would go through the normal battery of tests, the doctor would tell me I was in decent shape, and my employer would know that I'd be sticking around a few more years. No big deal.

There was, however, one particular test I dreaded (having to do with a scope), so I decided to put my negotiating skills to work. "What do I have to do to avoid that test?" I asked my doctor.

"If you stay on the treadmill longer than you did two years ago, I'll let you trade the test you want to avoid for this new EBT heart scan we're doing."

Properly motivated, I about killed myself on the treadmill, staying on for nearly half a minute more than I did during my prior session. I smiled all the way to the next testing station.

When we sat down in my doctor's office at the end of the morning, I expected to hear the usual accolades about my health. After all, at the last visit this same doctor had pretty much pronounced that I would live forever. I exercised, kept my weight down, avoided cigarettes, and kept the road rage to a minimum (given Atlanta traffic). I could stay on that treadmill as long as necessary to avoid certain tests. On the outside, I looked healthy.

I should have known something was up. My doctor wasn't engaging in the give-and-take banter we usually shared. "I'm afraid you've got a serious heart problem," he said, referencing my EBT scan. "I know this doesn't seem fair, because you've been taking care of yourself, but we've found a number of blockages in your arteries where the plaque has calcified, placing you in a high-risk category for a heart attack."

"Okay," I said, thinking maybe they had switched my EBT results with someone else's. "How bad is it?"

He hesitated. "You're in the highest-risk category there is," he said. "The normal score for a guy your age is about a 6, meaning there is a moderate amount of calcification in the arteries. Your score was 637."

This is exactly what Christ was telling the Pharisees. "You look healthy on the outside," He said—"whitewashed tombs," He called them in Matthew 23:27—"but inside your hearts have 'grown callous' [Matthew 13:15]. You do things to impress people, but your heart is growing cold and hard, further from God. Your heavenly Father cares about repentance and humility; you care about how many steps a man can take before he's violated a Sabbath law. You care about ceremonial purity; God cares about purity in the innermost thoughts. You guard the law, putting hedges around it; God says to 'guard your heart above all else, for it is the source of life' [Proverbs 4:23]."

Today many of us run around and do the same thing the Pharisees did two thousand years ago. We substitute activity for relationship. We work hard for God, attend church, and obey our own set of internally developed rules and regulations. To our friends, and sometimes to our family (though they're harder to fool), we seem pretty religious. We even enjoy the worship time at church, singing our hearts out to God. But in our quiet moments we have to admit that there's no real passion there.

We would rather watch television than spend time with the Lord. We can hardly remember the last time we really prayed. Our spiritual life is more duty than desire. Jesus's words are true of us:

These people honor Me with their lips,
> but their heart is far from Me.

They worship Me in vain,
> teaching as doctrines the commands of men.
> > (Matthew 15:8–9)

My doctor turned out to be not just a good physician but a good counselor as well. He reminded me how blessed we were to discover this condition now—with a test that wasn't even part of the original protocol. God allowed us to catch this, he said, so we can manage it with medication, monitoring, and further testing. And it's not like all those years of exercise were for naught. "If you hadn't kept yourself in shape, you probably wouldn't be here today," he said.

I was still reeling, but I decided to remain stoic in front of my doctor. I asked the question I knew my doctor wanted to hear. Once I asked it, he could outline a plan to help me manage my condition and impede any further calcification of the arteries. If I followed the plan and kept exercising, the heart would eventually build its own bypass system, turning minor arteries into major ones. But first I had to ask the question: "Okay, doc, what do I need to do?"

If you've got the same question on the spiritual front, keep reading. By the end of chapter six, we'll see the answer from a man who wasn't afraid to heal, even on the Sabbath.

4

WHAT'S YOUR SIGN?

A few years ago, my daughter Rosalyn was serving as a collegiate semester missionary in a Muslim city in the Middle East. She and her teammates would go door to door in apartment complexes, handing out copies of the New Testament in Arabic—the *Ingil*. They would knock on the door, knees trembling, and then calmly explain that they were followers of Jesus from America and had a gift for the apartment resident. Rosalyn and her friend had learned a little Arabic (a language so hard that they say it will be the language of heaven because it takes an eternity to learn it)—just enough to communicate if the residents didn't know English.

That semester, Rosalyn endured her share of rejection but also experienced the incredible hospitality of the local people. On a surprising number of occasions, the residents would invite the girls into the apartment, talk about spiritual matters, and feed the girls with the best delicacies in the house. Rosalyn learned what foods to eat and what foods to slide into her oversized handbag when her host stepped back into the kitchen. Rosalyn also learned that she had a heart for the city and these people.

When I visited Rosalyn for a week, she asked me to disciple one of the Muslim converts to Christianity, a *natour* (basically a combination doorkeeper/security guard for an apartment complex) whom I'll call Najeeb. I was excited and nervous as I sat down to talk with Najeeb—so anxious, in fact, that I knocked over my entire cup of coffee. I tried to clean up the mess I had made, but he insisted on doing it for me. I was immediately struck by the warmth and grace of Najeeb, a man who had already paid a high price among his family for his decision to follow Christ.

Firmly entrenched in my Western mind-set, I decided to start with some of the basic doctrinal truths found in the book of Romans. I would walk Najeeb through it step by step, reaffirming things such as our sin nature, the grace of God, and the atonement of Christ. You know—the fundamentals.

First, I established that Najeeb had read the entire New Testament, front to back.

"Two times," he said.

Good. "What did you think of the apostle Paul?" I asked.

Najeeb hesitated and gave me a puzzled look. "I don't remember the apostle Paul," he admitted.

I'm sure my jaw dropped, though I tried to keep a straight face. *You don't remember the apostle Paul?* I wanted to ask. *The guy only wrote about two-thirds of the New Testament! How can anyone read the entire New Testament (twice!) and not remember the apostle Paul?*

But before I could say anything that stupid, the Holy Spirit prompted me to take a different approach. "What do you remember about the New Testament?" I asked.

Najeeb's words stay with me still. "The resurrection of Jesus Christ," he said, his eyes dancing with the thought of it. "That is most remarkable."

Remarkable, indeed.

I had been sent to disciple this fledgling Christian. Instead, Najeeb had discipled me. In a sentence, he had zeroed in on the irrefutable core of the Christian faith, reminding me of what really matters. When you go to the land of Muhammad, when you talk to someone who will be asked to make a great sacrifice for his conversion to Christianity, you don't start with doctrines and theology—you start with the Resurrection.

It's the "sign" that Christ Himself selected when asked about His messianic credentials. It is not theory or conjecture, not doctrine or theology; it is the single most important event in human history. And like any other historical event, it can be verified.

In God's unfathomable wisdom, He gave us a bedrock foundation for our faith, an event that is at once undeniably supernatural and yet also subject to concrete historical proof. It's the certification of Christ's messianic mission—even more, His deity. It seals the promise of our own resurrection, a reason for hope beyond the grave. The Resurrection does all that and more. It is, in a word, remarkable.

NEVER SATISFIED

It must have been a miserable day in Galilee. The sun beating down on Jesus's back, dust and sweat forming a thin layer of grime on His skin. The crowd pressing in—a crush of people trying to touch Him. He'd been healing and preaching nonstop, with no time to eat.

Did Christ ever get irritable? You decide.

> Then some of the scribes and Pharisees said to Him, "Teacher, we want to see a sign from You."
>
> But He answered them, "An evil and adulterous generation demands a sign, but no sign will be given to it except the sign of the prophet Jonah. For as Jonah was in the belly of the great fish three days and three nights, so the Son of Man will be in the heart of the earth three days and three nights. The men of Nineveh will stand up at the judgment with this generation and condemn it, because they repented at Jonah's proclamation; and look—something greater than Jonah is here!" (Matthew 12:38–41)

I wonder how the scribes and Pharisees reacted. Irate? Maybe. Indignant? Sure, they had to be at least a little indignant. But I also picture smugness in their demeanor—a raised eyebrow, a cocking of the head. Like the lawyer who finally gets the witness to crack under pressure, maybe these leaders couldn't resist a smirk. *He's finally lost it,* they were thinking. *Gibberish. Give Him enough rope and He'll hang Himself. He's going to be like Jonah? Spit out of the heart of the earth instead of a big fish after three days? Right.*

Maybe this is why, a few chapters later, Matthew records essentially the same question, but this time with a side comment about the religious leaders' motivation: "The Pharisees and Sadducees approached, and as a test, asked Him to show them a sign from heaven"

(Matthew 16:1). And sure enough, He started talking about Jonah again. Like a good lawyer circling back to a killer question, the Pharisees trotted out the smirks and winks one more time.

And maybe this is the very thing that was driving Christ mad. Not the sweat on His brow or the crush of the needy, but the cynicism of His critics. Did they really need another sign?

Think about it. When they asked the first time, Christ had already healed the sick, cleansed a leper, cast out demons, caused the paralyzed to walk, calmed the wind and waves, and brought a young girl back from the dead! By the second time, He had added a few more equally impressive feats: feeding five thousand with five loaves of bread and two fish, walking on water, and healing all those who even touched the tassel of His robe.

And it's not like the scribes and Pharisees could claim ignorance. They hung around Christ every day, hounding Him with their questions, waiting for a slip-up so they could build their case against Him. No, they certainly saw their share of miracles. Yet still they pestered Him for a sign.

They didn't believe because they didn't *want* to believe. It wasn't a lack of evidence. And to make that point clear, Jesus was now pointing toward the most powerful evidence ever submitted—evidence that no open-minded jury could possibly ignore.

PROVE IT

As a trial lawyer, I've submitted dozens of cases to a jury. Some were strong. Others were so weak that they barely passed the red-faced test (if you can't make the argument without blushing from embarrassment, don't make it). But I've never had the luxury of trying a case as solid as the case for the physical resurrection of Jesus Christ.

Far greater jurists than I have reached the same conclusion. Lord Darling, the former chief justice of Britain's Supreme Court, expressed it this way: "In its favor as a living truth there exists such overwhelming evidence, positive and negative, factual and circumstantial, that no intelligent jury in the world could fail to bring in a verdict that the resurrection story is true."[1]

But let's not take Lord Darling's word for it (or mine, for that matter). In the next few pages, let's put his statement to the test. Is Lord Darling's statement hyperbole—the wishful thinking of a zealous man of faith—or is it true? Did Christ really do what He said He would—something that had never been done before? You be the "intelligent jury." I'll be the attorney giving the closing argument. I don't claim to be the best or most eloquent advocate for the Resurrection. But then again, if the case is as strong as I think it is, even a lawyer as pedestrian as I should be able to prove it.

LADIES AND GENTLEMEN OF THE JURY...

First, let me thank you for your patient and attentive service on this jury. You are the most important part of our justice system. (Lawyer's note: you *always* begin by buttering up the jury and telling them how important they are.) Soon this case will be yours and yours alone to decide. Our Founding Fathers, in their wisdom, set up a government in which the most important matters of justice, including issues of life and death, should be decided by average citizens like you, armed with the evidence presented to you, your common sense, and your life experiences. (Note to self: smile warmly.) I wouldn't want it any other way.

We start, of course, with this Book—exhibit A, the ancient Scriptures, especially the testimonies of the four gospel writers and the apostle Paul. The judge will instruct you, before you retire for deliberations, that the reliability of a historical document like this one should be judged by the following four factors: (1) how carefully and accurately it has been preserved; (2) how close in time to the events in question it was written; (3) whether the document is accurate with regard to statements and data we can verify; and (4) whether the document has the "ring of truth" to it. Let's go through these one at a time.

I'll start with its preservation.

THIS BOOK IS INDESTRUCTIBLE

The defense has suggested that the words of Scripture, as preserved today, cannot possibly be an accurate rendition of what the writers originally penned. A defense expert testified that we have none of the original manuscripts and lectured us at length about the fragility of ancient written materials such as papyrus and parchment. Poor storage conditions, lost documents, and inadvertent or intentional destruction of documents all contribute to the fact that many historical documents have vanished completely, he said. And then he reminded us, as if we were all elementary-school students, that there were no printing presses and no photocopiers, no foolproof way to copy or preserve manuscripts during the first century.

But I'm sure you'll also remember his lengthy cross-examination.

(Another smile here—this one of the cat-who-swallowed-the-canary variety.) He began by admitting that there are more than five thousand six hundred ancient Greek manuscripts verifying parts or all of the New Testament, with the earliest manuscripts dated less than fifty years from the original copies of the Gospels. In addition, there are eight to ten thousand Latin Vulgate manuscripts and another eight thousand or so in other languages, for a total of more than twenty-four thousand ancient manuscripts. (Stage directions to self: place the Bible directly in front of the jury box, then haul out from behind my counsel table several thousand-sheet bundles of copy paper.) Let's say that each single piece of this copy paper represents an entire manuscript. (Continue piling up packages of copy paper—two columns, each four feet high.) I'll place these about five steps away from the Bible, one step for each decade. (Stand back and give the jury a chance to look at this visual.)

Now, you've heard the defendant's expert admit that no other ancient book comes even close to the Bible in terms of the number of ancient copies that attest to its existence or the closeness in time of those copies to the original. For example, much of what we know about the ancient Romans comes from the history of Tacitus, written about AD 100. (Place a copy of his work next to the Bible.) There are only twenty ancient copies of his writings, with the earliest ones coming nearly one thousand years after the time of Tacitus. (Walk toward the back of the courtroom as I say this, with twenty sheets of copy paper in my hand.) If each step represents ten years, I would place these twenty pieces of paper about twice as far away from the jury box as the length of this courtroom. But just for the sake of illustration, I'll place them here by the back wall.

Not many copies, and not close in time, yet scholars still accept the historical accuracy of Tacitus's writings without question. The same holds true of Herodotus, a Greek scholar who wrote nearly four centuries before the birth of Christ. Nobody doubts that the works of Herodotus were faithfully transcribed and preserved, yet there are only *eight* ancient copies of his work, with the oldest copy dated almost *thirteen hundred years* after his death. I'll spare you the process of illustrating that. (Walk back to the jury box and give the jurors time to digest this.)

You'll also recall that we countered the defense testimony with our own barrage of expert witnesses who painted a picture of the miraculous preservation of the New Testament. In addition to the copies of the New Testament manuscripts themselves, there are more than eighty-six thousand quotations of the New Testament found in the writings of the early church fathers. These voluminous quotations are so thorough that all but eleven verses of the New Testament can be reconstructed from this material alone, all of which was written less than two hundred years after the life of Christ.[2]

So what? Why make such a big deal about the proliferation of ancient copies of the New Testament? Because the abundance of the early manuscripts and their closeness in time to the original writings allow us to verify the accuracy of the transcriptions down through the ages.

Unlike other ancient historical documents, which have few copies that can be cross-referenced, the thousands of copies of the New Testament confirm that the biblical account has been accurately preserved. By comparing these ancient copies with one another, we find that the text has no substantial variation among the copies, and what little variation exists pertains primarily to matters of spelling or word order. Not one variant has any bearing on a doctrine of the Christian faith.[3] (Place the Bible on top of the four-foot towers of copy paper—the foundation for our claims of accuracy.)

As our experts explained, the reason for this incredible accuracy is due in no small part to the meticulous transcription requirements for the early scribes. No word or letter could be written from memory without the scribe's having looked at the original text before him. Only the master original was used; no copies of copies were made. Letters per page were counted and verified. Each column had a specified number of letters. Each letter of the alphabet was counted for the entire scroll and verified against the master. The middle letter of the scroll was verified against the master. If there was one mistake made, the entire scroll was destroyed. In short, these conscientious scribes were antiquity's equivalent to a Xerox copy machine.

Every attempt to destroy the Bible has failed miserably. In AD 64 Nero led a massive persecution of Christians in Rome and blamed them for the great fire that destroyed much of the city. For almost three hundred years, Roman rulers persecuted and executed Christians, and Christian writings were indiscriminately destroyed. In AD 303, Diocletian declared that anyone discovered with a Bible would be immediately put to death. But no amount of Roman persecution or legislation could destroy what God intended to preserve. Copies of the Word of God were not only preserved but even grew exponentially in number.

Centuries later the French scholar Voltaire boasted that the Enlightenment school of thought would make biblical faith obsolete. Voltaire predicted that within one hundred years the Bible would disappear, implying that his own works would outlive Scripture. But new schools of thought also proved powerless against this life-changing Book. Today Voltaire's house is owned by the Geneva Bible Society, an organization that prints thousands of Bibles for distribution throughout the world.[4]

Voltaire's prophecy was no match for the prophecy uttered more than a thousand years earlier by the man who is at the center of this case. "Heaven and earth will pass away," said this carpenter turned nomad preacher who never penned a single word Himself, "but My words will never pass away" (Matthew 24:35). And here we are in a courtroom, two thousand years later, amazed at the resiliency of this carpenter's words—a resiliency that the carpenter Himself predicted.

So we see that the words of Scripture have been miraculously and accurately preserved.

IS THE BIBLE FIRSTHAND EVIDENCE OR HEARSAY?

The second issue you need to ask yourself about any ancient document is this: Was it written close in time to the events by those knowledgeable about the events? In other words, is it firsthand evidence written while memories were still fresh?

The vast majority of scholars agree that Mark was the first gospel written and that it was written within thirty years of the life of Christ.[5] They also believe that the gospels of Matthew and Luke, derived in large part from a common source document and from the gospel of Mark, were written a few years later. Luke authored his gospel sometime in the early sixties, and Matthew wrote his sometime in the seventies.[6] John, the last gospel written, probably came sometime after

AD 80.[7] By this time Paul had also penned his letters to the churches, eloquently defending the resurrection of Christ. In fact, some of Paul's writings can be dated back to the fifties, within twenty years of the Resurrection itself.[8]

You have heard testimony about other false "gospels," such as the Gnostic gospels of Mary and Thomas, written at the end of the second century AD, more than a hundred years after their alleged authors died.[9] Yet even these sources, which contradict much of the New Testament teachings on salvation and other critical doctrines of the faith, contain corroboration of the historicity of the Resurrection.[10]

And consider this: If the early church fathers wanted to fabricate gospel accounts of the life of Christ, would they choose authors as obscure as Luke and John Mark? Wouldn't they instead attribute these books to one of the well-known disciples of Christ? The relative anonymity of the gospel authors is a tribute to their authenticity.

But what about their accuracy?

DO EXTERNAL SOURCES CORROBORATE SCRIPTURE?

Another factor mentioned by the judge concerns the accuracy of the document as proved by outside sources. On this point you've heard extensive testimony of how modern archaeology and other corroborating historical sources affirm the accuracy of the New Testament narratives. You've seen how even reporters from secular publications realize this corroboration after surveying all the evidence. Consider, for example, this conclusion from a cover story by *U.S. News and World Report* on the accuracy of Scripture: "In extraordinary ways, modern archaeology has affirmed the historical core of the Old and

New Testaments—corroborating key portions of the stories of Israel's patriarchs, the Exodus, the Davidic monarchy, and the life and times of Jesus."[11] The article discussed recent archaeological digs that confirmed the existence of first-century places and events referenced only in Scripture. These include places like the Pool of Bethesda and the Pool of Siloam, and New Testament personalities, such as Caiaphas the high priest and Pontius Pilate.

You've also heard about many prominent archaeologists, such as Sir William Ramsey, who started as skeptics but found themselves converted as the rocks cried out. According to Ramsey, his initial mind-set was hostile toward Scripture: "I began with a mind unfavorable [to the book of Acts], for the ingenuity and completeness of the [German critical school of thought] had at one time quite convinced me."[12] But a slew of archaeological findings drove Ramsey to a different conclusion. "Luke's history is unsurpassed in respect of his trustworthiness," Ramsey wrote. And Luke should be "placed among the very greatest of historians."[13]

Ramsey's change of heart is typical of those who objectively investigate the historical and archaeological reliability of the New Testament. The critic becomes the converted.

And finally, let's consider the fourth factor the judge mentioned in his jury instructions.

DOES THE BIBLE HAVE THE "RING OF TRUTH"?

In other words, does common sense support the conclusion that exhibit A is a reliable historical document? Allow me to illustrate how this works.

Several years ago my wife and I were visiting relatives when my young niece came running into the house with a problem. She had a small rock stuck in her nose and couldn't get it out. Before lending her aid, my wife (you didn't think I was going to touch it, did you?) asked a question. "How'd that rock get up your nose to begin with?"

"The wind blew it there," our niece said.

Mmm. There's a story that doesn't pass our "sniffer" test. It doesn't have the ring of truth.

In a court of law, these types of stories come in two varieties. On close examination, either the story falls apart from lack of consistency and integrity, or the story seems too perfect for anybody to believe. True stories don't fit in neat little packages. Instead, they have the ragged edges that reflect the way things happen in real life.

For hundreds of years, scholars have scrutinized Scripture to a degree unknown to any other historical document. This extraordinary scrutiny has revealed no hint of fabrication.

If John Mark, writing on behalf of the apostle Peter, were making up his gospel, would he paint the disciples as scared and dejected followers of Jesus rather than courageous and majestic defenders of the faith? Would the Gospels reflect that John and Peter could not even stay awake with Jesus while praying in the Garden of Gethsemane on the night before the Crucifixion? When Christ was arrested, the apostles fled. Later Peter denied even knowing Christ. After the Crucifixion the disciples gave up and briefly went back to their former occupations. This hardly sounds like a fabricated legend designed to make its authors look good.

The first witnesses to the Resurrection, as recorded in the Gospels, were women. But this was a time when women were not allowed to give testimony in court. If the disciples fabricated the account of the Resurrection, would they have concocted a story in which women were the first to discover the empty tomb?

Would the gospel stories have been so overtly critical of the Jewish leaders and Roman authorities, the same groups who would persecute the church for the propagation of the Gospels?

The answers are no, no, no, and no. The Gospels are stories that show the warts of real life, because the Gospels are true. They have been miraculously preserved. They have proved themselves historically accurate. Exhibit A alone is proof positive of the Resurrection.

But there's much more.

THE EMPTY TOMB IS A HISTORICAL CERTAINTY, UNDISPUTED FOR MORE THAN A THOUSAND YEARS

The Christian movement would have been stopped in its tracks if the tomb of Christ were not empty. Peter's powerful sermon on the Day of Pentecost, when the early church was formed and three thousand souls were saved in one day, would have been categorically refuted by the existence of the decaying body of Jesus Christ in His nearby tomb. That tomb was within walking distance of the city that served as the birthplace of the church. A powerful church movement premised on the resurrection of its founder would never have flourished if the founder were in fact lying in a tomb a short distance down the road.

Even the opponents of Christianity, for more than a thousand years, didn't dare suggest the tomb was not empty. As you heard during the testimony, the earliest theories attempting to disprove the

Resurrection all assumed at least one uncontroverted fact—the existence of the empty tomb. Sure, they tried to explain it away by saying Jesus's disciples stole the body, but they *admitted* that the tomb was empty. In a court of law, the admission of an opponent is entitled to great weight. Especially when that admission is accepted as truth for more than a thousand years.

But that's not all. There's also...

LIVING PROOF AND A DYING DECLARATION

A third strand of positive evidence lies in the radically transformed lives of the disciples. I've tried enough cases to realize that witnesses lie for a number of reasons. Men and women tell lies to gain profit, to enhance their reputation, to gain political power, or for some other advantage. They lie to save their own skin. But men and women do not lie so they can then be tortured and burned at the stake. The notion that the Resurrection story could have been a fraud or legend concocted by the disciples is ridiculous when you consider the agony they endured for spreading it. Death has a way of revealing truth. Why would the disciples die for a lie?

And it's not just their willingness to stay strong in the face of death. History shows that the resurrection of Christ had the power to change lives. The mercurial apostle Peter became so terrified by the events surrounding the crucifixion of Christ that he denied even knowing Christ when confronted by a servant girl. Within weeks this same apostle boldly stared down Israel's leaders and proclaimed the Resurrection. Other timid and fickle pre-Resurrection followers became the lions of the early church. The self-serving disciples James and John, who had previously sought the highest places in a hoped-for political kingdom, became servants of others and humble leaders.

Something happened. Something changed them. No legendary myth could have done this. The millions of lives impacted by this historical event testify with one voice to the fact and the power of the Resurrection.

Put yourselves in the shoes of Peter for a moment. You are hauled before the Sanhedrin and warned to stop preaching in the name of Jesus, but still you preach. You see fellow believers stoned, whipped, and jailed for the faith. But still you persist. You are the leader of the church at Jerusalem and then the Syrian church in Antioch. Emperor Nero of Rome declares himself the "enemy of God," and you see Christians tied to posts, covered in wax, and then set ablaze to light the Roman roads at night. But still you try to convert others to take their place.

You are arrested and thrown in the Mamertine Prison in Rome—the infamous death cell. You are chained upright to a post in a chamber that is never cleaned and are left to stand in your own waste for nine months. Your only exposure to light occurs when the guards haul you out of prison to torture you. At any moment you can deny Christ, renounce His resurrection, and be released. But you refuse to become a traitor to your faith. You refuse to call the truth of the Resurrection a lie.

One day Nero hauls you before him to face execution. There you see your beloved wife, whom you have not laid eyes on since your arrest nine months ago. Renounce Christ and she will be spared; you will be released. Instead, you hold firm and Nero announces your sentence—crucifixion for you and your bride. Do you renounce now, at the very last opportunity?

No. Your resolve strengthens. You insist on being crucified upside down, because you are not worthy of dying like your Savior. As you are being led away, you look over your shoulder at your wife, gaze into her tearful eyes, and say, "O thou, remember the Lord."[14]

Can anyone seriously believe that Peter and the other apostles endured such treatment for a hoax? Are they the world's greatest and most long-suffering practical jokers? Did these simple fishermen have a warped desire to be martyrs for the greatest fraud ever perpetuated in human history? Or did they see the resurrected Christ with their own eyes and feel His power and courage in every sinew of their body?

This, then, is the evidence of a resurrected Christ. Miraculously preserved and meticulously prepared written documents. The unquestionable existence of an empty tomb. Disciples radically transformed. And the explosive emergence of the New Testament church within walking distance of where Christ was buried.

How do critics explain it away?

Well, you saw them on the witness stand and heard their alternative theories. You also saw them fidget and ramble on cross-examination.

FIRST, A LITTLE SOMETHING FOR CONSPIRACY BUFFS

The conspiracy theory is an explanation as old as the Resurrection itself. Even the Gospels record the beginnings of the conspiracy theory, stating that Roman soldiers were bribed to claim that the disciples stole the body while the soldiers slept (see Matthew 28:11–15). This theory was rejuvenated by deists during the eighteenth century but has today largely fallen out of favor with serious New Testament scholars. With good reason.

For one thing, it assumes that the disciples, this vagabond group of tax collectors, fishermen, and other ordinary men, could perpetuate the greatest fraud in world history. By what power did these unlearned disciples become so eloquent as to persuade thousands, and eventually millions, to become fooled by their fraud? How did they overpower the Roman soldiers who guarded the tomb with the penalty of death hanging over their heads for lack of diligence? How did they perform the miracles recorded in the book of Acts? The conspiracy theory requires the disciples to be persuasive men of deceit, fraud, hypocrisy, cunning, and eloquence. Nothing about the history of these men prior to the Resurrection suggests they had these capabilities.

But the theory is also fraught with internal contradictions. The soldiers claimed that the disciples stole the body while the soldiers slept. Even putting aside the fact that soldiers could be executed for sleeping at their post, the more obvious problem is this: if the soldiers were sleeping, how did they know who stole the body?

And what did the disciples gain by this alleged conspiracy? The privilege to follow their leader to an early and painful death? That's not the kind of reward that typically garners much conspiratorial enthusiasm.

So MAYBE IT'S ALL JUST A LEGEND

This is the idea that Christ might have been a prophet, but the stuff about His resurrection is just a legend developed later by His followers. Not surprisingly, this theory has a few problems of its own.

The primary shortcoming can be illustrated by my own high-school football career. For years I've been trying to develop the legend of myself as an unbelievable high-school quarterback. I'm so persistent that my kids joke about buying a T-shirt for me that says, "The older I get, the better I was." There's only one major problem with the legend I'm trying to develop. People are still alive who watched me play. Worse yet, the game films are available.

Believe it or not, some intelligent men spend much of their time trying to determine how long it takes for legends to develop. According to A. N. Sherwin-White, a noted historian of Greek and Roman history, it takes a minimum of two generations with no written documentation for a legend to develop that will supersede the facts. But the first gospel was written less than three decades after the death of Christ. According to Sherwin-White, there is no example of a legendary tale in ancient history that developed in so short a period of time. Never. When the story of the Resurrection was written, hundreds of witnesses to the crucifixion and ministry of Christ were still alive. As were hundreds of witnesses to His resurrection.

Think of it this way—it's now been about thirty years since I played high-school football. I might be able to get people to think I was slightly better than I really was. They might even believe we won a game or two more than we won. But would I have any chance of writing a book that convinced people I threw a miraculous pass the entire length of the football field that won a state championship? No, because those who watched my games would call me a liar. How much more difficult would it be to claim I came back from the dead and won the same game with the same miraculous pass? Such a claim wouldn't last a second.

Yet within the lifetime of thousands of witnesses who were contemporaries of Jesus, no fewer than five separate authors wrote about the Resurrection. This is not the way legends develop; it's the way history is recorded.

Moreover, the legend theory leaves too many facts unexplained. What about the martyrdom of the disciples? How do you explain the growth of the early church in the face of relentless opposition? How do you account for the empty tomb?

And for the next theory...

GET OUT THE SMELLING SALTS

The notorious swoon theory holds that Christ never actually died on the cross but simply fainted and ended up being revived in the cold, damp tomb before He appeared to His disciples. (Note to self: good time for an eye roll.)

Right.

The Romans were gruesomely efficient with crucifixion. Before Christ even made it to the cross, He would have been close to death, courtesy of a horrific Roman flogging. Alexander Metherell, a distinguished scholar with medical and scientific credentials who extensively studied the Crucifixion, described it this way:

> The soldier would use a whip of braided leather thongs with
> metal balls woven into them.... And the whip had pieces of
> sharp bone as well, which would cut the flesh severely.
>
> The back would be so shredded that part of the spine
> was sometimes exposed by the deep, deep cuts. The whipping

would have gone all the way from the shoulders down to the back, the buttocks, and the back of the legs....

A third-century historian by the name of Eusebius described a flogging by saying, "The sufferer's veins were laid bare, and the very muscles, sinews, and bowels of the victim were open to exposure."...

Because of the terrible effects of [Jesus's] beating, there's no question that Jesus was already in serious to critical condition even before the nails were driven through his hands and feet.[15]

After this beating, Christ faced the ultimate Roman punishment: death by crucifixion. Five- to seven-inch spikes were used to nail the victim to the cross through the wrists and through the feet. The spikes through the wrist would impact the median nerve and cause unbearable pain. Because the pain was indescribable in the language of the day, the Romans invented a new word—*excruciating*, which literally means "out of the cross."

As Christ suffered in excruciating agony, He died a slow death by asphyxiation. Listen again as Metherell describes the crucifixion process:

The stresses on the muscles and diaphragm put the chest into the inhaled position; basically, in order to exhale, the individual must push up on his feet so the tension on the muscles would be eased for a moment. In doing so, the nail would tear through the foot, eventually locking up against the tarsal bones.

After managing to exhale, the person would then be able to relax down and take another breath in. Again he'd have to push himself up to exhale, scraping his bloodied back against the coarse wood of the cross. This would go on and on until complete exhaustion would take over, and the person wouldn't be able to push up and breathe anymore....

Even before he died—and this is important, too—the hypovolemic shock would have caused a sustained rapid heart rate that would have contributed to heart failure, resulting in the collection of fluid in the membrane around the heart, called a pericardial effusion, as well as around the lungs, which is called a pleural effusion.[16]

By the time the soldier pierced the side of Christ with a spear, resulting in a gush of blood and water, there is no doubt that Christ was dead (see John 19:34). No one survived crucifixion.

Like proponents of the legend theory, swoonists generate their own share of unanswered questions. Even assuming that Christ miraculously survived the cross, how could a half-dead Christ, restored by the cool dampness of the tomb, rise up and remove the linen grave cloths (which had been immersed in seventy pounds of spices) from His body? How could He push away the two-ton rock that guarded the entrance to the tomb and then overcome the Roman guards, all while in a state near death?

When He appeared to the disciples, how did Christ walk through walls with His earthly body? And to top it all off, how did He recover so quickly and develop such incredible strength that within forty days He could jump into the clouds and fake the Ascension?

It takes more faith to believe in a Jesus who cheated death by swooning than to believe in One who conquered death by rising. Which brings us to a final theory.

AND THIS ONE'S FOR THE DOGS

Some would have us believe that Christ's body was laid in a shallow grave and eaten by wild dogs. This theory, in vogue now with certain members of the Jesus Seminar, is most notable for its lack of any evidentiary support.[17] It contradicts all the accounts from Scripture and has no positive evidence to support it. Plus, it doesn't answer the big-picture questions. What caused the change in the disciples? What generated the growth of the early church?

It doesn't even answer the smaller questions. The dogs ate all the bones, too? The disciples didn't bother to give Christ a proper burial, yet a little while later they were willing to die for Him? And if Christ's body were in fact placed in a shallow grave that dogs could access, don't you think it's unusual that nobody bothered to mention this until the late twentieth century?

(Note to self: big pause with major-league eye contact—make sure everyone's listening before continuing.)

IT ALL COMES DOWN TO THIS

The Resurrection. When the Pharisees asked Christ for a messianic sign, He predicted it. "As Jonah was in the belly of the great fish three days and three nights, so the Son of Man will be in the heart of the earth three days and three nights" (Matthew 12:40).[18] A few months later, just as He predicted, Jesus walked out of the tomb after three days and three nights, appearing to more than five hundred eyewitnesses.

The apostle Paul made it clear that our faith stands or falls with this one historical fact:

> If Christ has not been raised, then our preaching is without
> foundation, and so is your faith. In addition, we are found
> to be false witnesses about God.... If we have placed our
> hope in Christ for this life only, we should be pitied more
> than anyone.
>
> But now Christ has been raised from the dead, the first-
> fruits of those who have fallen asleep.... For just as in Adam
> all die, so also in Christ all will be made alive. (1 Corinthians
> 15:14–15, 19–22)

Did you catch that? If we believe in Christ for this life only—if we think He gave us some good teachings to live by but didn't really come back from the dead—then we have a pitiful faith. Why? Just ask the disciples or the millions of martyrs who went to the grave believing in the Resurrection. Following Christ in this life resulted in torture and a painful death. If not for the Resurrection, what did they gain?

"The blood of the martyrs," said Tertullian in the third century, "is the seed of the church." That blood is also proof of the Resurrection—an unbroken trail that extends from the original disciples to the present day. There have been more Christians martyred for their faith in the last hundred years than in all the other centuries combined. They died knowing that they would live again.

Those first-century Christians who *saw* Jesus die and then rise again knew beyond a shadow of a doubt that death was just a passageway. The rest of us gain the same assurance by looking back at this proven historical fact: Christ came back from the dead.

This is the one thing that separates Christianity from every other major world religion. We worship a risen Savior.

The word *verdict* is a Latin word that literally means "speak the truth." "What is truth?" asked Pilate. Three days later, Christ answered him. Today, let your verdict verify this ultimate truth—after three days in the grave, Christ arose.

You can bet your life on it. Millions already have.

5

GUILTY AS SIN

Hern ow can you represent someone you know is guilty?"
It's a question I heard often as a trial lawyer. Christian friends
would customize it: "*As a Christian lawyer,* how can you represent
someone you know is guilty?"

In response, I would start with a disclaimer. "I'm a civil litigator.
If I think my client's wrong, I settle. So I don't actually try to 'get
guilty people off.'" Then I would launch into a halfhearted defense
of the system. I'm an advocate, not a judge. My job is not to determine guilt or innocence; everybody is entitled to a vigorous defense…
that sort of thing.

"Well," my friends would reply, "I just don't think I could ever
represent someone if I knew for sure that person did it."

Whatever. To be honest, I'd heard it so often that I no longer
cared.

Then one day my entire perspective changed.

I was on a panel at Regent Law School with several other lawyers.
We talked about our particular areas of practice, trying to demonstrate

to students how we applied Christian principles to different kinds of law practices. I was the big-firm guy, besieged by high-pressure cases and demands for billable hours. "How would Jesus practice law in such a setting?" I asked the students. Then I explained how I had answered that question in my own experience.

I felt sorry for the public defender on the panel, a soft-spoken law-school friend of mine named Clark. After all, I was pretty sure that nobody in a Christian law school wanted to be a public defender. Ninety-nine percent of your clients are guilty, and none of them have any confidence in you. How good can a lawyer be if he or she isn't even paid by the client? The question I asked for my practice—How would Jesus act?—probably didn't even apply in this situation. A more relevant question might be this one: Would Jesus even take the job in the first place?

About two nanoseconds after Clark finished his introductory remarks, a law student stood up and asked the question we all knew was coming. "How can you represent these people when you know most of them are guilty as sin?"

Clark didn't even blink. He spoke softly, but his words carried the weight of a man who had devoted his entire professional life to serving those who could give nothing in return.

"When people come to the public defenders' office, they expect inferior lawyers," Clark explained. "They expect lawyers who are too busy and jaded to be good advocates. I try to surprise them with the quality of my representation the same way that Christ surprised me with the magnitude of His grace."

Then Clark paused for a moment and surveyed the audience,

making sure they didn't miss his next point. "I don't require them to be innocent for me to be their lawyer. And I'm so grateful that Jesus didn't require me to be innocent before He gave His life for me."

It felt like Clark had sucked the air right out of the room. You could see it in the students' eyes. Young men and women who only seconds before wanted to become big-firm lawyers were now considering the public defenders' office.

And Clark wasn't done yet. "If Christ were alive today, you might find Him advocating for clients like mine. After all, that's what He did two thousand years ago, and it's what He's been doing ever since."

IN THE VERY ACT

John tells the story simply but leaves no doubt about the woman's guilt:

> Early in the morning [Jesus] came again into the temple, and
> all the people came to Him; and He sat down and taught
> them. Then the scribes and Pharisees brought to Him a woman
> caught in adultery. And when they had set her in the midst,
> they said to Him, "Teacher, this woman was caught in adul-
> tery, in the very act." (John 8:2–4, NKJV)

"In the very act," the Pharisees said. "Caught in adultery," John wrote.

Could you be more specific? we wonder.

Who was she with? Why didn't they bring him, too? How did

they catch her "in the very act" in the first place? Were the Pharisees spying on this woman like voyeuristic Peeping Toms? Was she a prostitute? Was this a one-night stand or an ongoing affair?

And where is John's sense of the dramatic? No self-respecting storyteller today would say it so plainly. Especially a scene like this one! Paint the picture, John. I mean, you don't have to take us into the bedroom, but at least explain how she got involved with this man in the first place. How did the emotional connection begin? What was her reaction when the Pharisees caught her?

But none of these details are forthcoming, because the Holy Spirit didn't prompt John to write them down. And perhaps before we even study the reaction of Christ, we can learn something from the straightforward way John tells this part of the story.

The simple lesson is this: the Bible doesn't glorify sin. John pulled no punches—she was caught "in the very act." But he didn't dwell there either. This is not a story about adultery; it's a story about grace. And mercy. And Christ as our advocate.

Can you imagine what Hollywood would have done with this? Maybe the scriptwriter would have glamorized the affair so much that we would be upset with Christ. What do you mean, "Go and sin no more"? She *loves* him. She can't just walk away.

Or at the very least, the affair would form the heart of the movie. An hour and a half on the allure of her lover; the slow burn that resulted in this one-night stand. Ten minutes on Christ's defense. A postscript might mention her changed life.

Why? Because Hollywood understands sex appeal.

But it's not just Hollywood. Church members sometimes share "prayer requests" or concerns about others in the church, rich with detail about the sins committed. Occasionally Christians give testimonies that wow fellow believers with details about how bad they were before they met Christ. A sense of shame is replaced by an almost boastful recitation of what a mess they were prior to conversion. A popular religious Web site has even lampooned this behavior, issuing a fake press release about "testimony crimes"—burglaries and drug offenses committed by teenagers so they can have a jazzier testimony after they repent and come to Christ.

John didn't play that game. She was caught in adultery, he said. Just the facts. No glamorizing the sin that put Christ on the cross. The sin that breaks God's heart. That hurts the ones we love.

The sin is just a prelude. The adultery of this woman can be established by one simple sentence. She was guilty. Aren't we all? The Cross is the real story. The world may choose to glorify sin, but those of us in Christ have something far more interesting to talk about. In the church, we should do what John did: focus on the main character—the Savior waiting patiently in the temple to do what no other man could do. That's where the miracle occurred. That's where the story is.

How Cool Is This?

It seems an unlikely setting for one of the greatest legal defenses of all time. There was no media buildup, no trial-of-the-century hype. The defendant was not O. J. or Michael Jackson or even some first-century celebrity. In fact, the very appeal of this defendant is that she was so ordinary—less than ordinary, even—and reminds us of ourselves on our worst day. If she could get off, we think, there's hope for the rest of us.

It took place not in a *courtroom* but in the temple *courtyard*. But the most peculiar aspect of the case, and for the defense attorney the most troubling, is that the accusers were also judge and jury. It would be like defending former president Bill Clinton on his impeachment charges if the only senators allowed to vote were Republicans. Or defending Alabama Judge Roy Moore, the Ten Commandments judge, in front of a jury of ACLU lawyers. Any normal defense attorney would scream about the inequities in the process...while trying to cut a deal.

But this was no normal defense attorney.

The day began innocently enough, with Jesus heading to His Father's house to do what He did best. "At dawn He went to the temple complex again, and all the people were coming to Him. He sat down and began to teach them" (John 8:2).

We can picture the tranquil scene. The sun orange on the horizon, not yet bearing down with the intensity of midday heat. A few hard-core believers arriving at the temple. Early-morning persons— you know the type. These are the folks who wake without an alarm clock, put on a fresh pot of coffee, and have their morning devotions before the rest of us stumble out of bed. Like that old ad for the army: "We get more done before breakfast than most people do all day." On this day these early birds are about to witness something so extraordinary that we still marvel at it two thousand years later.

The town is buzzing with the events of the day before. Halfway through the Feast of Tabernacles, Jesus had strolled into this same temple courtyard and begun teaching. At first, He awed the crowd. This untrained carpenter taught with uncommon authority! But then things got crazy. He accused the crowd of wanting to kill Him. They hollered back that He was demon possessed. They started choosing sides, for and against. Could this be the Messiah? Many in the crowd thought so. "When the Messiah comes, He won't perform more signs than this man has done, will He?" (John 7:31).

At the height of the controversy, in the heat of the day, the chief priests and Pharisees sent the temple police to arrest Christ. The religious leaders had heard enough. They had seen enough. They had been ridiculed and outfoxed enough. It was time to take decisive action against this troublemaker from Galilee.

But the police came back empty-handed.

"Why haven't you brought Him?" asked the chief priests and Pharisees.

The police answered, "No man ever spoke like this!" (John 7:45–46).

Eventually, everyone went home.

That was yesterday. Today promises more adrenaline-laced excitement. At the very least, more incredible teaching from this new prophet. So it is no surprise when His followers, some gadflies, and a few curious onlookers start gathering at the temple early. They want a good seat for a day that promises plenty of action.

To their surprise, Jesus is already there at the temple, ready to teach them. Imagine this—an intimate moment with Christ. Not the great prophet standing on the mount to project His wisdom to thousands or getting offshore in a boat so He wouldn't be crushed by the crowd, but a teacher sitting with His followers in the dry Judean dirt and discussing deep truths that make their hearts burn within them. Maybe a few have questions: "Um, Jesus, remember that time You said..." or "Jesus, I always wondered about that one parable..."

Maybe He smiles and tousles the hair of a child as He unveils an eternal truth.

Intimate time with Jesus, a man who claims to be the Messiah! Word spreads quickly, and the crowd grows. A gospel writer would later describe it this way: "All the people were coming to Him" (John 8:2). "All the people" includes the scribes and Pharisees—in spectacular fashion. They bring the guest of honor with them, a woman who was caught in the act of adultery, probably the night before.

As they parade her in, she's embarrassed, fearful, half-clothed. Her long dark hair covers her face. She hangs her head and slumps her shoulders. They haul her to the courtyard, one of the larger Pharisees on each side, and with a final gruff yank on her arms, they toss her in front of Christ. She stands there, feeling the eyes of a hundred onlookers boring into her, condemning her. She dares not look up.

She doesn't say a word in her own defense. No complaints about the man not being brought with her. No rationalizations about how lonely she had been or how wrong the Pharisees were for meddling in her private life. She was caught in the act, humiliated in front of her hometown, and now she has to face her punishment.

Stoning. Rocks flying at her from all directions. At first the throws would be ceremonial and formal—the religious leaders aiming a few large stones at her head. Soon the mob would join in with perverse pleasure—angry men and women fulfilling the judgment of the Lord. Others would join in for sport. She would initially cover her head, but the relentless barrage would take its toll. The pain would drive her to her knees. More stones would rain down, including large ones hoisted by two men, the thud of heavy rocks hitting the mark as she curls into a fetal position. Snapping bones, spurting blood, her face unrecognizable by the time she dies.

Stoning. A slow and painful death designed to deter others. Her punishment for one night of pleasure.

" 'Teacher,' " the religious leaders say to Jesus, " 'this woman was caught in the act of committing adultery. In the law Moses commanded us to stone such women. So what do You say?' They asked this to trap Him, in order that they might have evidence to accuse Him" (John 8:4–6).

The glee of the Pharisees is nearly as palpable as the pain of the woman. They know the soft spot Christ has for sinners, but they also know His reverence for the Law of Moses. This is their ultimate trick question. *Have you stopped beating your wife?*

Perhaps the woman is popular in the city. Perhaps she has small children. But the Law of Moses knows no exceptions on this point. Her punishment is clear. If Christ will say the word, the stoning will begin. The Pharisees hold the rocks in their right hand—their throwing hand. There is no wiggle room on this one. The Pharisees themselves caught her in the act. They have her right where they want her.

And so does God.

The woman is desperate. An acknowledged sinner with nowhere to turn but to Christ. She brings no excuses, just repentance and a cry for mercy so hopeless she can't even verbalize it. Maybe she glances in shame at Christ. More likely, she keeps her eyes glued to the dusty ground in front of her, a silent plea to the man who holds her fate. A man who could never resist the prayers of those who admit how desperately they need Him.

And so the best defense attorney of all time goes to work.

He starts with a procedural matter, the first-century equivalent of the Miranda warning. Is she guilty? Sure. But Christ has a jurisdictional trick up His sleeve. He stoops and writes in the dirt with His finger. When the leaders persist in questioning Him, He stands and says to them, "The one without sin among you should be the first to throw a stone at her" (John 8:7).

In hindsight the strategy seems brilliant. But let's freeze frame it right there. Put yourself in this woman's place. What kind of defense is this? "It's okay—go ahead and kill her. Just make sure it's done the way Moses says. We'd hate to have you stone throwers get out of order."

Can there be any doubt that at least one of the Pharisees will throw that first stone? These are the folks whom Christ called "whitewashed tombs," the ones who never noticed the log of sin in their eye as they fretted over the speck of sin in someone else's. Certainly none of them is sinless. But equally certain, some of them will at least claim to be.

But Christ isn't finished. In an exceptionally cool move of studied nonchalance, He squats and writes in the dirt again. The Pharisees, who just seconds before were gloating about their ironclad case, drop their stones and walk away. Just like that, it's over!

WHAT DID JESUS WRITE IN THE DIRT?

Some say He just doodled, giving the Pharisees time to think about their sins. But this seems out of character for the Pharisees, considering the way they acted on other occasions. It seems to me that Christ must have written something so compelling in the dirt, something so irrefutable, that the Pharisees didn't dare go forward with their plan. There are a few possibilities.

Some Bible scholars believe that Jesus wrote the names of the women with whom the Pharisees had affairs. Perhaps the names of their illegitimate children. Perhaps the amount of money they plundered from the temple. Whatever He wrote, the message was clear— I've got the dirt on you (so to speak). Stone her and you'll be next in line. Their shame compelled them to abandon the case.

But there is another possibility, one that would make any trial lawyer proud. Later in Scripture we learn that the Jewish leaders had no jurisdiction to impose the death penalty on their own. It's the reason why the Sanhedrin marched Jesus in front of Pilate rather than just disposing of Him by themselves. "It's not legal for us to put anyone to death," the Jewish leaders told Pilate (John 18:31). Historians tell us that the Jews were probably allowed to enforce the Mosaic Law, including the death penalty, in an ad-hoc way, through spontaneous stonings carried out by the people. But members of the ruling Jewish establishment, and especially members of the Sanhedrin, had a higher duty. They were required to act at all times in strict accordance with Roman law or lose their limited privileges of self-rule on religious issues.

This may explain why they tried to get Jesus to cast the first stone. If He did, He would be violating Roman law and they could drag Him before the proper authorities for punishment. If He didn't, then this self-proclaimed Messiah would be catering to Roman law rather than upholding the revered Mosaic Law. Either way, they had Him.

Until He started writing in the dirt, that is. Yes, maybe He wrote about their sin. But maybe, after telling one of them to throw the first stone, He started writing Roman statutes in the dirt, reminding *them* of the cost of insurrection and effectively turning the dilemma right back on His accusers.

Either way, this much is clear: Jesus relied on a procedural defense. A technicality, if you will. But an extremely effective one.

Scripture says the scribes and Pharisees left "one by one, starting with the older men" (John 8:9). I picture Christ writing on the ground, inscribing details about the men's secret sins or citations to the Roman laws prohibiting them from imposing the death penalty. The older men step forward one by one, read what is written, drop their rocks, and leave. The younger men see this and follow suit. And then, perhaps, Christ sweeps some sand and dust over what He has written, obscuring the details so that even His disciples will never know.

The crowd holds its collective breath. The woman has not moved—and now she's left to face the Messiah for one of Scripture's most tender moments. Jesus stands up and says to her, "Woman, where are they? Has no one condemned you?"

"No one, Lord," she answers.

"Neither do I condemn you," says Jesus. "Go, and from now on do not sin any more" (John 8:10–12).

And there you have it. "Not guilty. You are free to go. Neither do I condemn you."

AND STILL HE PLEADS

The adulteress in this story is us. Christ made that clear early in His ministry. "I tell you, everyone who looks at a woman to lust for her has already committed adultery with her in his heart" (Matthew 5:28).

Never lusted? That's okay. Under the Mosaic Law, they stoned murderers too. "You have heard that it was said to our ancestors, Do not murder, and whoever murders will be subject to judgment. But I tell you, everyone who is angry with his brother will be subject to judgment" (Matthew 5:21–22).

Have you ever been angry with your brother? If not, then let's go one step further and talk about your enemies. How are you doing at *loving* them? Not tolerating them. Not praying that God will judge them. But really loving them and seeing them the way Christ does. "I tell you, love your enemies and pray for those who persecute you" (Matthew 5:44).

There's also that nasty little matter of taming the tongue. Do you have that under control? "If anyone does not stumble in what he says, he is a mature man who is also able to control his whole body" (James 3:2).

I could go on, but the point is obvious. "There is no one right-eous, not even one.... All have sinned and fall short of the glory of God" (Romans 3:10, 23). We stand before Christ as the adulteress did—guilty, speechless, ashamed. Caught in the very act.

Satan is the accuser. Dragging us before Christ. Pointing out our shortcomings. Lining up the witnesses to testify against us. Count 1: That harsh word to our co-worker. Count 2: The secret rejoicing when someone else failed. Count 3: Gossip. Count 4: Envy. Count 5: A lack of faith. Count 6: Staying silent when our friend needed to hear about Christ. Satan has it all written down—legal pads full of notes—and there is no denying it.

The punishment is worse than stoning. Eternal separation from

God. Hopelessness. Weeping and gnashing of teeth. Millions of years marching by in eternity while our hearts yearn to see God, knowing it can never happen.

As you stand there staring at the ground, contemplating this judgment, you sense the slightest movement in front of you. You glance up quickly, anxiously, then look back down. Did you see that right? You look again, confirming. Squatting before you is Christ, index finger extended, writing in neat block letters on the ground. *The cross,* He writes. *Debts paid.*

You realize this is no procedural defense. You can still see where the thorns punctured His brow and the nails pierced His wrists. He took your punishment—every lash, every beating, even the death warrant. You bow your head in awe and shame.

He rises and walks to you. He stands in front of you and lifts your chin, gazing at you with compassionate eyes. "Where is your accuser?" He asks. "Is there anyone left to condemn you?"

You turn around. There's no one there. It's just you and Jesus. You look left and right. Wasn't Satan there in all his contemptuous glory just a few minutes ago? "No one, Lord," you say.

Jesus's eyes sparkle. "Neither do I condemn you," He says. "Go and sin no more."

You smile. And nod. And weep.

Humbly, you bow before Him.

"If anyone does sin, we have an advocate with the Father—Jesus Christ the righteous One. He Himself is the propitiation for our sins, and not only for ours, but also for those of the whole world" (1 John 2:1–2).

6

THE LAW AS TASKMASTER

A major part of getting the right information is asking the right question. This is certainly true of lawyers, and never more so than when a case hangs in the balance during cross-examination. Good cross-examination is an art form, as the lawyer leads the witness down a primrose path to exposure and disgrace. But unskilled cross-examination is…well, embarrassing. The lawyer runs headlong into a trap of his or her own making, leaving the client to wonder how a lawyer this bad could cost this much.

Examples of bad questions abound. The following were reportedly asked by real lawyers in real cases tried in the Commonwealth of Massachusetts. Imagine paying your lawyer a few hundred bucks an hour to ask questions like these:

Q: How far apart were the vehicles when the accident occurred?

A: Huh?

Q: Ma'am, how many children do you have?

A: Four.

Q: How many are girls?

A: Four.

Q: How many are boys?

The following is the examination of a store clerk testifying about a convenience-store robbery:

Q: Please describe the perpetrator of the crime.

A: About six foot four, two hundred forty pounds, with a beard.

Q: Male or female?

And here is my all-time favorite. This criminal defense attorney apparently didn't have much of a case, because he was trying to prove that maybe the victim wasn't really dead when the coroner started the autopsy. I know, it's a bit of a stretch, but you do your best with what you have:

Q: Doctor, did you check for a pulse before you started the autopsy?

A: Of course not.

Q: Did you check for any vital signs before you started the autopsy?

A: No, that's ridiculous. I never check for vital signs before I do an autopsy.

Q: Then isn't it just possible that the victim was still alive when you started?

A: That's absolutely ridiculous. Of course not.

Q: How can you be so sure?

A: Because his brain was on my desk in a jar.

(I assume that the next question was the lawyer's lame attempt at humor—it's impossible to tell from just reviewing the transcript. If so, the question backfired.)

Q: Couldn't he have been alive nevertheless?

A: I guess he could've been alive and practicing law someplace.

Ouch. I'm sure the lawyer wished he could take those questions back the minute they left his mouth. And you can bet that the jury came back with a guilty verdict. An ill-advised question led to a surprising answer, sealing the fate of the defendant.

That's basically the way it went down two thousand years ago, when an astute first-century lawyer decided to take on a witness a thousand times more dangerous than the Massachusetts coroner. Unlike the Massachusetts lawyer, the one questioning Christ at least asked the right question.

Unfortunately, he asked it with the wrong attitude. "Just then an expert in the law stood up to test Him, saying, 'Teacher, what must I do to inherit eternal life?'" (Luke 10:25).

This is the same question that Jesus would later be asked by a rich young ruler: "Good Teacher, what must I do to inherit eternal life?" (Luke 18:18). It is the seminal question that has been on the hearts of people throughout history: What must I do to live forever? It is, no doubt, the right question.

It's not surprising that Jesus would be asked this question, not just once, but at least twice. The surprising part is the Teacher's response.

OBEY THE LAW

Fast-forward a few thousand years and put the question in today's context. What if a lawyer asked you that question? What if a rich young ruler did?

Let's say, just for the sake of argument, that a young millionaire who had recently been elected to the United States Senate came up to you and, in all sincerity, wanted to know what he needed to do in order to have eternal life. What an opportunity! Think of the good this person could do for the kingdom.

You'd probably say a quick prayer something like this: "God, help me not to blow it here. This man can do a lot for You. Help me to clearly explain the death of Jesus as payment for his sins and the grace of God that is the basis for eternal life."

You would probably feel a little like a hair-spray salesman if Donald Trump had just walked in the door. Whatever else happens, you've got to close the deal. If you've taken the right evangelism-training course, you probably know just how to do that. At the very least, you may have heard an evangelist or pastor working hard to close the deal every Sunday morning.

"Today is the day of salvation! You're not guaranteed tomorrow! You could leave this worship service and get in a car accident and never make it home. Don't leave here without getting things right with Christ! All you have to do is ask Him into your heart as your personal Lord and Savior. He's already paid the price for your sins. Just come forward as we continue to sing this hymn—all four verses—and one of our altar counselors will pray the sinner's prayer with you."

Some churches take a different approach. They've found that asking people to come forward during an altar call can be embarrassing and create hesitation. Those churches have substituted decision cards that people can discreetly fill out and slide into the offering plate.

Then there are churches who have tailored their message to generate the greatest possible response. These fast-growing churches like to emphasize the attractive aspects of Christianity that help us deal with life's challenges. Wasn't it Christ who said, "My yoke is easy and My burden is light" (Matthew 11:30)? They focus on taking away people's excuses and overcoming people's hang-ups. For too long, these churches claim, Christianity has been known for what it's against. It's time to stop emphasizing the negative parts of Christianity—eternal judgment, sacrifice, service, Christ's exclusivity. Christ came to empower. He came to set free. God is love. Christ is love.

It's all good.

But if we're not careful, our desire to see people come to Christ will cause us to emphasize least the very thing that Christ emphasized most. We will want to minimize the cost of Christianity so that decisions for Christ and church membership will increase, but Christ seemed intent on practically driving people away. Have you counted the cost? Are you truly repentant? Are you ready to forsake family and wealth and comfort for the sake of the gospel? If not, you're not ready to become a Christ follower.

Yes, salvation is a gift. But until we realize our desperate need for this gift and our own unworthiness, we aren't ready to receive it.

Don't get me wrong. I'm not criticizing churches that conduct altar calls or use decision cards. In fact, as you'll see later in this chapter, I'm a big fan of requiring people to make these types of prayerful commitments. But not just for the sake of notching up another baptism or decision statistic. Dr. Henry Blackaby once told me that we make following Christ seem so easy in many of our churches that members walk the aisle or fill out decision cards without really understanding what it means to make Christ Lord of their lives. "By doing this, we make them twice the citizens of hell," Blackaby said, "content in a false assurance of salvation."

Think about that. *Twice the citizens of hell.* We allow people to think they can be saved without real repentance. Or we lead them to believe that the act of walking the aisle or joining the church somehow makes them a citizen of heaven. Christ, on the other hand, never even issued the invitation until He knew the heart was ready.

With Nicodemus, a man broken and ashamed, Christ talked about being born again. But with the rich young ruler, a man full of himself and his own good works, Christ first had to make the man see that all his good works could never earn him a place in heaven.

WHAT MUST I DO TO BE SAVED?

"Good Teacher, what must I do to inherit eternal life?" the ruler asked (Luke 18:18). Notice the mind-set: what must I *do?* For him, it was a given that salvation could be earned. It wasn't a question of *whether* he needed to do something; it was just a question of *what* he needed to do.

For the Good Teacher, class was now in session. "You know the commandments," Jesus said. Then He listed some:
- "Do not commit adultery."
- "Do not murder."
- "Do not steal."

- "Do not bear false witness."
- "Honor your father and mother" (Luke 18:20).

Jesus wasn't surprised by His student's pious response: "I have kept all these from my youth" (Luke 18:21). *Mmm,* thought Jesus, *I'll bet you have.*

Note how Jesus incorporated some of the Ten Commandments into His question, but only those that govern our relationships with others. Conspicuously lacking from Christ's list is the first commandment: "Do not have other gods besides Me" (Exodus 20:3). An oversight or an object lesson?

> When Jesus heard this, He told him, "You still lack one thing: sell all that you have and distribute it to the poor, and you will have treasure in heaven. Then come, follow Me."
>
> After he heard this, he became extremely sad, because he was very rich. (Luke 18:22–23)

Jesus's followers were amazed when the rich young ruler turned and left. And it wasn't just because Jesus had let a good prospect get away. (Can't you hear Judas: "Lord, think of the donation this man could have made to our treasury!") The disciples believed that riches were a sign of God's favor. If a rich man couldn't inherit eternal life, who could be saved?

Jesus had an answer to that question as well: "What is impossible with men is possible with God" (Luke 18:27).

Far from teaching salvation by works, Jesus was demonstrating that even the most pious man could *never* work his way to God. Here was a man who would put most of us to shame. Since his youth, he had not lied once or stolen anything. He had honored his father and mother. But he still had a fatal flaw. The man loved money. And using the Law as a tutor, Christ demonstrated that even this man, just like the most reprehensible tax collector, could not possibly *earn* eternal life.

The apostle Paul phrased it this way:

Well then, why was the law given? It was given to show people how guilty they are. But this system of law was to last only until the coming of the child to whom God's promise was made....

Well then, is there a conflict between God's law and God's promises? Absolutely not! If the law could have given us new life, we could have been made right with God by obeying it. But the Scriptures have declared that we are all prisoners of sin, so the only way to receive God's promise is to believe in Jesus Christ.

Until faith in Christ was shown to us as the way of becoming right with God, we were guarded by the law. We were kept in protective custody, so to speak, until we could put our faith in the coming Savior. (Galatians 3:19, 21–23, NLT)

Through the rich young ruler, Jesus was demonstrating that salvation cannot be earned. "Keep the Law," Jesus said.

"I have," replied the ruler.

Really? Then it shouldn't be any problem to demonstrate you have no god besides Yahweh, so why don't you just give all your money to the poor?

But the ruler went away sad, not yet ready to accept the free gift of salvation. Jesus didn't beg the ruler to come back or ease the requirement that the ruler first give away everything he owned. Salvation is a free gift, but it comes with irrevocable preconditions. It is *always* preceded by genuine repentance—something that doesn't come naturally to rich young rulers. Or lawyers, for that matter. A small thing called pride keeps getting in the way.

The Pride of Charles Finney

He would become one of the greatest revival preachers this country has ever seen. But few who knew him in the fall of 1821 would have believed it. Least of all his pastor, George W. Gale.

As far as Gale was concerned, the same keen intellect that made young Charles Finney such an intimidating force as a small-town lawyer in Upstate New York also kept Finney from embracing the childlike faith necessary to enter the kingdom. Finney would debate Gale for hours, stumping the Princeton-trained theologian with unanswerable questions. Finney would also cross-examine his neighbors with his simple yet deadly logic, causing many Christians in town to turn aside when they saw him coming in order to avoid the barbs of the town's leading skeptic.

So Finney took his skepticism straight to church, confounding the Christians on their own turf. "If God answers prayers that are consistent with His will, then why has He withheld a great revival?" Finney would ask. "You have prayed enough since I have attended these meetings to have prayed the devil out of [town], if there is any virtue in your prayers. But here you are praying on, and complaining still."[1]

It's no wonder that George Gale, and most of the others, gave up on Charles Finney, saving their prayers for someone more reasonable.[2] But several younger members of the congregation, including Finney's future wife, stubbornly refused to quit praying for him. And eventually the same powerful logic that Finney used against the church led him to an unwelcome but unavoidable conclusion: there are no answers to life's questions apart from Christ.

In time, like the New Testament lawyer and the rich young ruler before him, Finney asked the only question that truly mattered: "What must I do to inherit eternal life?" In typical Finney style, he didn't just ask the question; he obsessed over it, losing sleep and sliding into depression as he struggled to gain favor with God. On a particularly emotional autumn morning, Finney decided that he would become saved that day or die in the attempt. He retreated deep into the woods, determined to get alone with God, ashamed to have the townsfolk see him in such a state.

In the woods, as he cried out to God, it seemed as if his prayers rose no farther than the treetops. In fact, the harder he prayed, the less effective his prayers became. Suddenly, like the bright light that blinded Saul on the road to Damascus, a flash of insight leveled Finney, driving him to his knees before God.

Right there the revelation of my pride of heart, and the great
difficulty that stood in the way, was distinctly shown to me.
An overwhelming sense of my wickedness in being ashamed
to have a human being see me on my knees before God took
such powerful possession of me that I cried at the top of my
voice, and exclaimed that I would not leave the place if all the

men on earth and all the devils in hell surrounded me. "What!" I said, "such a de-graded sinner as I am, on my knees confessing my sins to the great and holy God; and ashamed to have any human being, and a sinner like myself, find me on my knees endeavoring to make peace with my offended God!" The sin appeared awful, infinite. It broke me down before the Lord.[3]

Confessing his sins, including the pride that drove him deep into the woods in the first place, Finney found the truth of a promise he had once mocked: "If we confess our sins, [Jesus] is faithful and just to forgive us our sins and to cleanse us from all unrighteousness" (1 John 1:9, NKJV).

Finney's conversion was so dramatic and complete that it turned the town upside down, ironically answering the same prayers for revival that Finney had ridiculed. On the first day after his conversion, Finney literally put down his lawyer's briefcase and picked up a preacher's Bible.

The first person he met that morning was Judge Wright, the senior partner in Finney's firm and his mentor in the law. Instead of the usual talk of cases or politics, Finney told the judge about his conversion. Judge Wright dropped his jaw in astonishment, then hung his head and left the office without saying a word. (A few days later, the judge also came to Christ in the same woods. He returned to Finney, shouting, "I've got it! I've got it!" Then he fell to his knees and praised God.)

The second man Finney met at his office that morning was a deacon from the church with an important case Finney was scheduled to argue that day. "You'd better settle that case," Finney advised him.

"What do you mean?" asked the startled deacon. Finney had never mentioned settlement before.

"I have a retainer from the Lord Jesus Christ to plead His cause, and I can [no longer] plead yours," replied Finney.

The deacon settled his case. From that day forward, Finney devoted every ounce of his energy and skills to preaching the Word. "I was quite willing to preach the gospel. In fact, I found out that I was unwilling to do anything else.... No labor...could be so sweet and no employment so exalted as that of holding up Christ to a dying world."[4]

It seemed that everywhere Finney preached, God sent revival. Throughout New York, in town after town, the worst sinners became "trophies of grace" as revival transformed the town. Not surprisingly, Finney the lawyer did not preach like the professional clergy. Instead, he instituted a series of "new measures," speaking in plain and potent language, treating the congregation like a jury in need of persuasion. He called on people to repent and make a decision for Christ, instituting "anxious seats" in the first few rows of the church for those who were under deep conviction for their sins. At the end of a week of revival meetings, he would call those in the anxious seats to take a public stand for Christ, confessing their sins and their need for a Savior.

These new measures incurred the wrath of the established church. But the fierce criticism only seemed to inspire Finney and fuel his commitment. Finney became more determined than ever to call men and women to take a public stand, motivated by his own experience and the explicit words of Christ: "I say unto you, Every one who shall confess me before men, him shall the Son of man also confess before the angels of God: but he that denieth me in the presence of men shall be denied in the presence of the angels of God" (Luke 12:8–9, ASV).

Finney's anxious seats became the precursor to the modern-day altar call, another device used to call sinners to a public profession. But the new measures of Finney's day have become the discarded old measures of today. Which is fine. Techniques and methodologies change. The anxious seats of Finney's day morph into the decision cards of today. Yet sooner or later they all lead to the same place—a public profession of faith in Christ.

And some things don't change. Like the cost of following Jesus. Or the need to confess our sins. Or what it means to repent.

And always there's that small but deadly demon called pride.

" 'What!' " cries Finney. " 'Such a de-graded sinner as I am, on my knees confessing my sins to the great and holy God; and ashamed to have any human being, and a sinner like myself, find me on my knees endeavoring to make peace with my offended God!' The sin appeared awful, infinite. It broke me down before the Lord."

When is the last time we sinned? "If we say, 'We have no sin,' we are deceiving ourselves, and the truth is not in us" (1 John 1:8). When was the last time we truly repented of those sins? When was the last time we humbled ourselves before the Lord and others, so heartbroken for our sin that we didn't care if all the people on earth and all the demons in hell showed up and made fun of us?

If it's been a while, then maybe it's time to go and take a place on the anxious seat. Every time we harden our hearts to the conviction of the Holy Spirit, allowing pride to have its way, we become a little less like Finney and a little more like that self-justifying lawyer who questioned Christ many years ago.

WHO IS MY NEIGHBOR?

He came pretending to ask questions when he secretly thought he had all the answers. The lawyer's question was a test, Scripture says. I'm sure the man had his flow charts all worked out in his head, the way any good lawyer would on cross-examination. *I'll ask Jesus how to inherit eternal life. If He says this, then here is my next question; if He says that, then I've got a different path to take Him down.* The man probably spent hours working on his if-then scenarios. Tripping up Christ would be the ultimate feather in this lawyer's hat, making him the Johnnie Cochran of his generation.

In a matter of seconds, Christ demolished every one of the lawyer's plans, putting the man on the defensive, turning the lawyer into the witness.

"Teacher, what must I do to inherit eternal life?" the lawyer asked.

"What is written in the law?" Jesus asked him. "How do you read it?" (Luke 10:25–26).

The question seemed harmless enough. Not exactly something the lawyer had planned for, but certainly he couldn't refuse to answer such a basic question without looking silly. He probably didn't even hesitate: "Love the Lord your God with all your heart, with all your soul, with all your strength, and with all your mind; and your neighbor as yourself" (verse 27).

Jesus responded, "You've answered correctly.... Do this and you will live" (verse 28).

And here's where it starts to get tricky. Perhaps this lawyer was notorious for the way he treated those outside the Jewish race. Or perhaps he was a ruthless prosecutor for the Sanhedrin, and the listeners all knew that this man had not followed the Golden Rule—treating others as he would want to be treated.[5] We don't know the exact circumstances, but we do know this—Christ hit another bull's-eye. He had used the lawyer's own words to convict him, and the lawyer knew it. So the lawyer turned defensive. "Wanting to justify himself, he asked Jesus, 'And who is my neighbor?'" (verse 29).

Can't you see Jesus smiling in response? *I thought you'd never ask.* "Jesus took up the question" and then launched into the parable of the good Samaritan, a response that perfectly illustrates the intellectual genius of Christ.

The story is painfully simple, yet it plays itself out on so many different levels that it still staggers us two thousand years later, mind numbing in the brilliance of its multifaceted message. Like the Hope Diamond, it reflects light however it is turned, each angle revealing a slightly different luminescence, each more beautiful than the last.

It is, for starters, a story a mere child could understand:

A man was going down from Jerusalem to Jericho and fell
into the hands of robbers. They stripped him, beat him up,
and fled, leaving him half dead. A priest happened to be going
down that road. When he saw him, he passed by on the other
side. In the same way, a Levite, when he arrived at the place
and saw him, passed by on the other side. But a Samaritan
on his journey came up to him, and when he saw the man,
he had compassion. He went over to him and bandaged his
wounds, pouring on oil and wine. Then he put him on his
own animal, brought him to an inn, and took care of him.
The next day he took out two denarii, gave them to the

innkeeper, and said, "Take care of him. When I come back I'll reimburse you for whatever extra you spend."

"Which of these three do you think proved to be a neighbor to the man who fell into the hands of the robbers?"

"The one who showed mercy to him," he said.

Then Jesus told him, "Go and do the same." (Luke 10:30–37)

So much for legal loopholes about the definition of neighbor. If a hated Samaritan could be considered a neighbor, then our obligation to love our neighbor extends to all humankind. But if you see the parable as doing *only* that, you are missing much of the wisdom of Christ. It's like saying the purpose of the ocean is to make boats float. Sure, boats can stay afloat in the buoyant salt water, but there's so much more going on under the surface, a marine environment that supports two-thirds of the world's living organisms. Diving a little deeper, we will discover that Christ's parable has multiple meanings on multiple levels, an eloquent testimony to the genius of the Teacher.

Close to the surface, so obvious that we sometimes miss it, this parable is about what it takes to really love your neighbor as yourself. Allow me to illustrate with a brief example of what happened to me the day before I started writing this chapter.

FRED IN THE DITCH

I was sitting on a park bench near the beach, minding my own business, waiting for my wife to finish some souvenir shopping. An unshaven man, slightly older than me, walked over to the bench and sat down.

"How's it going?" I asked.

"You don't want to know," he said.

I was facing a moment of truth. On the one hand, he was right. I really didn't want to know. I had books to write, work to do for the mission board, and law-school classes to prepare for, not to mention the urgent need to get my wife out of the souvenir shops. I was on vacation, trying to relax. Plus, it's not like our family doesn't get involved in hands-on mission work, trying to help people less fortunate than us. It's just that on this particular day I was experiencing what James Dobson calls "the principle of limited tears"—a defense mechanism that keeps us from emotionally investing in everyone's problems in order to avoid an emotional meltdown.

So, no, I really didn't want to know.

On the other hand (and with lawyers, there's always another hand), I was preparing to write this chapter on the good Samaritan. Naturally, I was a little concerned that if I just blew this guy off, God might strike me dead on the spot. Since you're reading this book, you can assume that didn't happen.

"You're wrong," I said. "I really do want to know."

That's all the encouragement the man needed. Fred (not his real name) had been thrown out by his second wife about a month before, after nearly thirteen years of marriage. He turned to the bottle and soon lost everything. This well-educated man now slept on the beach and bummed meals from a local church while searching for a rehab clinic that would take him in. Two days before I met him, Fred had been accepted into a six-month program only to find out the next day that they didn't have room for him after all.

The night before I met him, Fred had been soaked in a downpour at the beach. "Normally when it starts to rain," he explained, "I'll go up to the taxi stand, and there are a couple of those guys who let me sleep in the backseat of their cars all night. But last night the storm moved in so quickly that I got drenched before I woke up."

Fred looked up at the sky and shook his head. "Kick me while I'm down, why don'tcha?"

Not surprisingly, Fred was fighting a nasty cold.

I spent the next half hour defending God, encouraging Fred, and making a friend. Before I left, I tried to give Fred some money to help him out. Initially he refused, but he eventually accepted the money and broke down crying. I made Fred promise not to give up on that rehab program.

Having shared this whole experience (I'll call it "the parable of the self-aggrandizing author who just lost any reward he might otherwise have received in heaven for this"), let me ask you a question: Who proved to be the neighbor in that story?

If you guessed me, then you need to remember that lawyers love to ask trick questions. You may want to read the parable of the good Samaritan again. If you answered the taxi drivers, then move to the front of the class.

What I realized, a few days after my encounter with Fred, is that the parable of the good Samaritan is really a parable of *involvement*. The good Samaritan didn't throw money at the problem and leave. He personally bandaged the man's wounds. The wounded man rode the good Samaritan's animal while the Samaritan walked alongside.

The good Samaritan took care of the man at the inn and took responsibility for the man's debt.

Even the taxi drivers fell short of this standard, but at least they got involved in Fred's life. As for me, I took an easier way out—a few minutes of empathy and a little money. Better than what the priest did in Christ's example, that's for sure. But is that really the way I would want to be treated if I were Fred? Is that the way Christ would have treated him?

My point is simply this: as an example of the type of conduct Christ expects from us as we try to love our neighbors as ourselves, the parable of the good Samaritan still packs a pretty powerful punch.

EQUALITY UNDER THE LAW

If we dive a little deeper, there's plenty going on in the next stratum of meaning. There we discover that Christ's parable not only serves as an unparalleled model for personal behavior, but it also illuminates the true intent of the Old Testament Law. As Christ said, "Don't assume that I came to destroy the Law or Prophets. I did not come to destroy but to fulfill" (Matthew 5:17).

It's that same issue about the letter of the Law and the spirit of the Law that we discussed earlier. The religious leaders focused on the letter of the Law and, in particular, on what the Law forbids. But here Christ focused on the spirit of the Law, emphasizing not the things we should avoid but the type of person we should strive to become. In the process, He demolished the racial and ethnic prejudice that had come to characterize the interpretation of the Law favored by the Pharisees.

Christ chose a Samaritan as His hero. Most Jews looked down

their noses at the Samaritan half breeds—Israelites who married Gentiles and thus polluted the lineage and the faith of Israel. Under the Law, Israel's national blessing depended on maintaining racial purity, avoiding interracial marriages that might lead its citizens away from Jehovah. But Jesus's parable presaged a new day. "A person is no longer a Jew or a Greek, a slave or a free person, a male or a female, because all of you are one in Christ Jesus" (Galatians 3:28, ISV).

It was shocking enough when Jesus demonstrated tolerance toward the Samaritans by ministering to the Samaritan woman at the well. But this? Elevating this unnamed Samaritan over a priest or a Levite—how scandalous!

Christ's message to the lawyer was as plain as it was bold: "The one who fulfilled the spirit of the Law was the Samaritan, not the priest, not the Levite (and certainly not you—by asking the question about who your neighbor is, your heart has been revealed). The Samaritan is someone to be emulated, not just tolerated. You self-righteous pure-blooded Jewish lawyers need to start acting more like this humble Samaritan."

Lineage doesn't matter, the Great Equalizer was saying. Priestly qualifications don't matter. Racial boundaries don't matter. The Samaritan had the only credentials that did matter: a soft heart and willing hands. God is no respecter of persons—He loves everyone equally. And so should we.

Deeper still, there's more.

SAVING GRACE

At its core, this parable is really not an object lesson about the Law at all. Instead, it is a beautiful picture of God's grace. Turn the diamond one way and we are the passersby on the side of the road. Will we help? Are we willing to get involved? What kind of neighbor are we?

But turn the diamond again and we are the wounded traveler. Robbed of our dignity and hope by sin, left bleeding and helpless on the side of the road, unable to continue on our own. Isn't this the real message from Christ's interaction with both the rich young ruler and the self-righteous lawyer? They couldn't make it on their own. They tried to obey the Law—and worked a lot harder at it than most of us—but it took Christ only a few seconds to dismantle their facade and expose their sin. They failed to measure up. Just like us.

The Law is the priest and Levite walking by on the other side of the road, leaving us right where it found us—beat-up and naked, half-dead. But grace is the Samaritan, giving us what we don't deserve. Christ stops and binds our wounds, pouring on oil and wine. He takes us to a resting place and puts our sins on His account. He shows us compassion, not because we deserve it, but because we need it.

Having provided so great a salvation, Jesus then looks at us with the same piercing eyes He fixed on that lawyer two thousand years ago. "Who showed mercy to you?" Jesus asks us.

"You did, Lord."

His response? "Go and do the same."

7

JESUS TAKES THE FIFTH

If someone mentions the Fifth Amendment, we think of scoundrels and crooks hiding behind a wall of silence. Corporate CEOs facing congressional investigations: "Senator, I respectfully assert my rights under the Fifth Amendment to the United States Constitution." Criminal defendants sitting arrogantly in court: "Ladies and gentlemen of the jury, you may not infer guilt or make any adverse findings based on the defendant's failure to take the witness stand." As far as most of us are concerned, the right to avoid self-incrimination is a shield for criminals, something that makes it harder to convict the guilty. We conjure up images of a smug O. J. Simpson or Scott Peterson. And we've never heard of "Freeborn John" Lilburne.

Freeborn who?

Lilburne, the grandfather of our current Fifth Amendment, lived in England during the first half of the seventeenth century, a time of intense religious persecution. He described himself as "an honest true-bred, freeborn Englishman that never in his life loved a tyrant nor feared an oppressor."[1] Others paint a less-flattering picture.

Leonard Levy, an expert on the common-law origins of the Fifth Amendment, describes Freeborn John this way: "He was obstreperous, fearless, indomitable, and cantankerous, one of the most flinty, contentious men who ever lived. As one of his contemporaries said, if John Lilburne were the last man in the world, John would fight with Lilburne and Lilburne with John."[2]

Lilburne was an equal-opportunity antagonizer. He quarreled with the Catholic Church and defied the interrogators of the Star Chamber (a corrupt ecclesiastical court in which the Catholic Church coerced confessions from Protestant troublemakers). Not long after Oliver Cromwell and the Protestants took over, he challenged them as well. He thumbed his nose at the ecclesiastical courts, at the House of Commons, and at the House of Lords. He was arrested numerous times and stood trial for his life on four occasions. He became a leader of the "Levellers"—libertarians who believed that all men in England should be treated the same under the law.

His rise to notoriety began in 1638 when he was hauled before the Star Chamber. Lilburne was accused of shipping seditious books into England. All the court needed was a confession.

For the Star Chamber, this would pose no problem. They would simply make Lilburne take an oath ex officio and then ask him questions under oath about his activities. The inquisitors knew that this would place men of conscience like Lilburne under an impossible dilemma—admit their guilt or lie under oath and risk the wrath of God.

But Lilburne, steeled by his study of both the Magna Carta and John Foxe's *Book of Martyrs,* refused to take the oath. No problem. The Star Chamber sentenced him for *that*—ordering that he be placed in the pillory (a.k.a. the stocks—a wooden frame with holes through which the victim's hands, legs, and head are placed so he or she can be ridiculed by the public) and then jailed until he took the oath. Oh, and in addition, Lilburne was to be brutally whipped as he walked the two-mile road to the pillory.

They whipped him more than two hundred times, flaying his back the entire way. But Lilburne maintained his defiance, berating those who tortured him. The man who wouldn't speak in the Star Chamber wouldn't shut up as his captors lashed him with all their might. When they put him in the stocks, instead of maintaining a humiliated silence as did other convicted prisoners, Lilburne lectured the crowd, turning the stocks into his own bully pulpit.

He became a folk hero overnight.

He spent years in prison, stoically maintaining his refusal to testify before the Star Chamber, serving more than four months in solitary confinement. He made good use of his prison time, authoring nine pamphlets that made the case for the rights of all freeborn Englishmen. When political changes resulted in the abolishment of the Star Chamber, Freeborn John became a free man once again.

But eventually Freeborn John ended up on the enemies list for Cromwell and his government as well. In March 1646 he was summoned before the House of Lords for criticizing one of its members. He refused to answer the charges against him, maintaining his silence as a means of protesting *their* jurisdiction.

When they threw him in jail and later recalled him for further questioning, he barricaded his cell. His jailers broke down the barricade and literally dragged him before the House of Lords. Once there, Freeborn John stood upright, which presented another problem, since every British subject was expected to kneel as a sign of respect. Since he refused to kneel, he was placed in solitary confinement.

After weeks of this, they brought him back before the House of Lords, where again he refused to kneel. Frustrated, they decided to read the charges against him anyway. Like a stubborn child, Lilburne stopped his ears with his fingers, refusing to acknowledge the authority of the House of Lords to even read the charges against him. Lilburne was sentenced to an indefinite period of time in prison and served nearly a year before public opinion compelled his release.

Less than a year following that release, Cromwell had Lilburne arrested again, this time on charges of sedition for a pamphlet Lilburne had allegedly authored. Lilburne refused to mount a substantive defense, instead spending his time bickering with the judge about his rights as a freeborn Englishman. Lilburne demanded the right to subpoena witnesses, the presumption of innocence, the right to remain silent, and most important, the right to trial by jury. When a jury was finally impaneled to hear the case, including the refusal by Lilburne to even answer questions about whether he had written the pamphlet in question, it took the jury less than one hour to acquit him.

Though he eventually found himself banished from England on pain of death, Lilburne and his "freeborn rights" became the basis for many of the liberties enshrined in the Bill of Rights that Americans enjoy today. No freeborn Englishman, he claimed, should have to answer questions that might provide evidence against himself. Even saying whether or not he wrote a pamphlet would be an "un-Englishman-like deed." If the rights and privileges of his birthplace meant anything, they meant that he didn't have to subject himself to that type of questioning. He would rather be whipped and banished from his homeland than abandon his principles.

Did you ever wonder if Christ felt the same way? The scribes, Pharisees, and lawyers relentlessly questioned Him. Jesus used those occasions to teach timeless truths about His kingdom or to chastise His questioners. But in reality, He had no duty to respond to them at all. If being born an Englishman (or an American) means you have no obligation to subject yourself to cross-examination, then how much more so for one born of God?

He was with God in the beginning.
All things were created through Him,
and apart from Him not one thing was created. (John 1:2–3)

What right did the Pharisees and lawyers—created beings—have to question the Son of God? Paul would later ask the question this way: "Who are you—anyone who talks back to God?" He answered this rhetorical question with another: "Has the potter no right over His clay?" (Romans 9:20–21).

The potter, of course, can do whatever He wants with the clay. And though we don't like it, given our information-rich, "I have a right to know everything" society, the plain fact of the matter is that God has no duty to answer all our questions.

GOD ANSWERS TO NO MAN

In this chapter we'll be exploring the one occasion prior to His final trial when Jesus "took the Fifth." He did it cleverly, by asking a question of His own—"Where did John's baptism come from? From heaven or from men?" (Matthew 21:25)—and when the Pharisees couldn't answer His question, He refused to answer theirs. (They had asked Him to explain where His own authority came from.) For now, I want to focus on how the Pharisees and onlookers must have felt when Jesus asserted this divine Fifth Amendment right—and how we feel when God exercises His prerogative not to explain His actions to us.

It's a hard right to swallow. Sure, we instinctively know that God's ways are not our ways. God, being God, will do things and allow things that our finite minds cannot comprehend. Intellectually, we get that. And we know that the proper response is to trust God anyway. In a reverse-psychology kind of way, the very fact that we can't understand everything God does tends to prove His existence.

Sigmund Freud and other secular thinkers have accused the church of manufacturing God. Karl Marx called God the "opiate of the people." But a manufactured God—a product of our own minds—would be eminently comprehensible. We would make up a human-sized god who always made sense, not some transcendent being who asks us to trust Him even when He doesn't seem to make sense.

But knowing this intellectually and applying it in the crucible of life are two very different things. If we're honest, we'll have to admit that when God takes the Fifth, it generates the same visceral reaction that occurs when we see a criminal "hide" behind the right to remain silent. What's going on here? Why won't God answer? What's He trying to hide? Is there really a God at all? If He loves me, then why has all this stuff happened?

SURVIVING WHIRLPOOLS OF GUILT

Memorial Day in Upstate New York, my childhood stomping grounds, meant only one thing: the General Clinton Canoe Regatta. According to the local chamber of commerce officials, it was one of the biggest, if not *the* biggest, marathon canoe race in the world. I can sense that maybe you're not impressed, since you've probably never even heard of marathon canoe racing, but it was the only thing we had to brag about other than the National Baseball Hall of Fame.

The race started in Cooperstown and ended seventy miles later in Bainbridge. Eight hours on the wily Susquehanna River, seventy hard strokes a minute, three large dams where you had to get out and sprint with your boat up and down a muddy embankment. Hundreds of two-person teams from all over the United States and Canada. Fifty thousand spectators. The seventy-miler was a rite of passage for a kid from Delhi.

I completed my first race when I was a senior in high school. My partner and I finished fifth out of more than a hundred entries in the amateur class, shocking everyone, most of all ourselves. I then found that college life and marathon canoe racing didn't mix, particularly since I had more important things to do than train three or four hours a day (like finding a wife). But my first year out of college, I was ready to return with a vengeance, and I found just the partner to join me.

His name was Bruce Merritt. He was completing his senior year in college. Class president. Pre-law major who had already been accepted at a number of prominent law schools. A great friend. But most important for canoeing purposes, the guy was a paddling machine. He was

Rocky with a canoe paddle. He'd go for a long run in the morning, then we'd paddle for a couple of hours in the afternoon, then Bruce would lift weights at night.

Bruce would paddle up front and be our primary motor. I would try to match him stroke for stroke in the back, but my main job would be steering. I knew the river. Bruce was an animal. It was going to be a very good year.

We caught a break with the weather. We were bigger than most teams and, with Bruce up front, a little more powerful. There had been a lot of rain in the days before Memorial Day. The river was high and fast, giving an edge to the bigger tandems. We started off shaky on the upper part of the river—a snaky, narrow, snarling stretch of water with hairpin turns, tricky currents, and a lot of overhanging branches. We tipped over once but eventually got in a zone and started passing people.

By the halfway point, we had moved up to seventh.

"How're you doing?" I asked Bruce. We were approaching "twin bridges," a dangerous stretch of water where two railroad bridges had collapsed in the water, creating an unpredictable series of whirlpools and eddies.

"I feel great," Bruce said.

Good, I was thinking, *'cause I'm dying back here.*

We came flying through the first set of rapids near the twin bridges. We cut the corners sharp in the S turn, still looking to make up ground on the teams ahead of us. We leaned hard, placing the slick racing boat on its side, the edge of the gunwale just a few inches from the water. We were tracking the fast inside edge of the current, a risky spot that rewarded us with maximum speed. Without warning, we hit a strong crosscurrent that yanked us with terrifying force toward the bridges that were half-submerged in the water, stirring up vicious whirlpools all around them. I shouted a couple of commands and we corrected—overcorrected, really—and everything went bad.

The raging current whipped us sideways. We hit a whirlpool and flipped. The rapids kicked me out toward one bank and Bruce toward the other. I grabbed the boat, flipped it, jumped back in, and started paddling furiously to get Bruce. He saw his paddle in the middle of the current and instinctively dove for it.

A whirlpool caught him and pulled him under. He popped back up. "I need some help here. I'm getting tired."

I was still too far away, paddling like a madman to reach him. Too slow! My arms felt like lead. He grabbed his paddle and stretched an arm toward me.

"Hang on!" I yelled.

The current dragged him under again.

"No!" I jumped from the boat and swam toward the whirlpool. I flailed around in the muddy water, looking for Bruce. Searched desperately with my eyes. Yelled for help. Dove under and found nothing. Popped up and yelled. Dove under. Popped up. Felt myself tiring, the whirlpool pulling at me. I managed to get back to my boat and hang on. Rescuers dragged me to shore.

They later found Bruce's body several hundred yards down the river.

I started asking the *why* questions in the ambulance on the way to the hospital. I was in shock, still trying to comprehend what had happened. I couldn't believe that God would allow my best friend to die. Later that day I saw inconsolable pain on the face of his girlfriend. A few days later, I saw a father bury his only son. The questions haunted me for weeks, months, the better part of a year.

Why Bruce, God? I mean, the guy had so much potential. Class president. Honor student. Everybody loved him. He would have been an awesome lawyer. Why so young? And why, God, did you spare me and not him? Why did the boat kick out on my side of the river? Why did his paddle have to get stuck in the whirlpool?

Please help me understand, God. Because now I'm the one drowning in the guilt and loneliness and confusion.

In response, the heavens were silent.

WE'RE IN GOOD COMPANY

Job knew what it felt like to have unanswered questions.

Born thousands of years before Christ, this man's suffering is legendary. He lost everything within a matter of hours—riches, family, health. The pawn in a celestial chess match between God and Satan. Most of the book of Job is a recounting of his misery and questioning, as Job and his friends try to figure out what in the world God was thinking. He questions God. Challenges God even. And refuses to be comforted by the clichéd responses of his friends.

But the book concludes with God crashing Job's pity party and immediately turning the tables. God makes it clear that He has no intention of answering Job's questions. Listen to God's "I'll ask the questions here" speech (and remember, this is a big, booming voice coming out of a whirlwind):

Who is this who obscures My counsel
with ignorant words?
Get ready to answer Me like a man;
when I question you, you will inform Me.
Where were you when I established the earth?
Tell Me, if you have understanding.
Who fixed its dimensions? Certainly you know!
Who stretched a measuring line across it?
What supports its foundations?
Or who laid its cornerstone
while the morning stars sang together
and all the sons of God shouted for joy? (Job 38:2–7)

For four chapters, God asks Job questions that no man can answer.

Would you really challenge My justice?
Would you declare Me guilty to justify yourself?
Do you have an arm like God's?
Can you thunder with a voice like His? (Job 40:8–9)

Think about this. If anybody ever had a right to question God, it was Job. He lived a righteous life but lost everything. Even his wife and friends turned against him. Our suffering is nothing compared to this poor guy's. *How does a loving God allow this to happen?* Job wanted to know. *What have I done to deserve this?*

But God never answers. His whole speech, in fact, is designed to show He doesn't *have* to answer. This is Freeborn John Lilburne times a thousand. Times a thousand thousands. God created us. He loves us. He knows what's best for us—not just for this life but for eternity. With Job, God knew that He was getting ready to restore everything Job lost. Twice over.

But in the meantime God had no obligation to answer Job's litany of questions.

Many of us have claimed that when we get to heaven we're going to ask God a few questions. We don't understand it now, and we'll want to get an answer to it then.

I used to say that about Bruce's death. As if I would storm through the gates of heaven and demand an explanation.

These days, I doubt it.

If I'm reading my Bible correctly, when we make it to heaven, we'll do the same thing every other man and woman has done when they have found themselves in the awesome presence of a holy God. We'll be so busy worshiping that all our questions will probably just melt away. Even Job learned that it's hard to maintain a prosecutorial posture in the presence of the God of the universe.

> Then Job replied to the LORD:
> I know that You can do anything
> and no plan of Yours can be thwarted.
> You asked, "Who is this who conceals My counsel
> with ignorance?"
> Surely I spoke about things I did not understand,
> things too wonderful for me to know.
> You said, "Listen now, and I will speak.
> When I question you, you will inform Me."
> I had heard rumors about You,

but now my eyes have seen You.

Therefore I take back my words

and repent in dust and ashes. (Job 42:1–6)

"I've heard rumors about You," Job said, "but now my eyes have seen You." And when that happened, Job fell on his face and repented.

It's normal for us to ask the *why* questions. We'd be lying if we denied that we sometimes have the same thoughts Job had.[3] *What's going on? Who's in charge here?*

But here's some tough advice that I had to learn the hard way, and I don't know how to say it nicely: Don't think God owes us an answer. You may be devastated, disappointed, and depressed, but if you're waiting for God to give you an explanation, it's probably not going to happen. Sometimes it will, but not always. God is under no obligation to make sure we understand the whys and wherefores of His plans. He isn't searching for a person who *understands* everything; He's looking for people who will trust Him even when they *don't* understand everything. *Especially* when they don't understand everything.

It comes down to the issue of authority. Either God is in charge of our lives or He's not. Either God has sovereignty in this world or He doesn't. If we acknowledge God's authority only when what He is doing makes sense, then we're not really giving Him control of our lives. Instead, we're trying to reduce God to our finger puppet— obligated to operate within the confines of our own intellect and our own conception of what is fair and what is reasonable.

Such was the mind-set of the religious leaders who constantly confronted Christ. They believed more in their own intellect and tradition than in the power of God revealed through Christ. In their minds, Christ had a duty to answer their questions and a duty to provide answers that fit their world-view.

Turns out they were wrong on both counts.

WHO GAVE YOU THIS AUTHORITY?

Matthew starts the story this way: "When [Jesus] entered the temple complex, the chief priests and the elders of the people came up to Him as He was teaching and said, 'By what authority are You doing these things? Who gave You this authority?'" (Matthew 21:23).

As usual, it helps if we put this in context. The day before this confrontation, Jesus had entered Jerusalem on what we now call Palm Sunday, making His triumphal entrance riding a donkey, just as the prophet had predicted. A huge crowd spread their robes and palm branches on the ground ahead of Him while everyone shouted,

> Hosanna to the Son of David!
> Blessed is He who comes
> in the name of the Lord!
> Hosanna in the highest heaven! (Matthew 21:9)

What a sight this must have been! Think about it. The Son of God riding on a donkey, feet nearly dragging on the ground. The crowd going ballistic. Dust and noise spreading like a mushroom cloud from the makeshift parade. "The whole city was shaken," Matthew wrote. People were asking: "Who is this?" And the crowds kept telling them: "This is the prophet Jesus from Nazareth in Galilee" (verses 10–11).

From there, Jesus headed straight to the temple, overturning the tables of the corrupt moneychangers and the chairs of those selling doves for sacrifices (at an enormous profit). He lashed out at them verbally as well as physically: "It is written, My house will be called a house of prayer. But you are making it a den of thieves!" (verse 13). Not exactly the warm and fuzzy Christ we see depicted in most Bible pictures.

He healed the blind and lame, got into an argument with the chief priests and scribes (shocker), and then went to the village of Bethany to spend the night. When He returned to the temple the next day, the chief priests and elders were ready. "Who gave You this authority?" they wanted to know.

Notice how the question has changed. There is no longer any doubt that Christ *has* unusual authority. The question now is where it came from. When this cat-and-mouse game started, the religious leaders had challenged Christ's assertion of authority at every turn. "You can't forgive sins," they challenged.

"Oh yeah?" said Christ. "Watch this!" And He healed the paralytic.

"We want a sign of your authority," they announced.

"An evil and adulterous generation demands a sign," He responded.

And right after He defended the adulterous woman, they went after Him again. "You are testifying about Yourself," the Pharisees said. "Your testimony is not valid" (John 8:13).

As usual, Jesus was not intimidated by this criticism. "Even if I testify about Myself...My testimony is valid, because I know where I came from and where I'm going.... Even in your law it is written that the witness of two men is valid. I am the One who testifies about Myself, and the Father who sent Me testifies about Me" (John 8:14, 17–18).

Now public opinion has shifted. Jesus has healed enough, taught enough, and overturned money tables enough so that the issue of *whether He* has authority is no longer open. And before we plow ahead, it might be wise to remind ourselves that, when He left the earth, He delegated His authority to us. That's right—you and me! The weak, the foolish, the poor, the downtrodden. The ones whom Christ entrusted with the greatest mission of all time: "With my authority, take this message of repentance to all the nations, beginning in Jerusalem: 'There is forgiveness of sins for all who turn to me.' You are witnesses of all these things" (Luke 24:47–48, NLT).

We would do well to remember this when the authority of our beliefs is attacked almost daily by the post-Christian insistence that we can't know anything with certainty. Experiential "truth" rules—it might work for you, but that doesn't mean it works for me. Even our language is peppered with disclaimers and qualifiers, a conversational way of hedging our bets so that someone won't think we're dogmatic or judgmental or close-minded. College campuses are replete with courses that question everything and belittle those who cling to absolutes. Law schools don't teach black-letter law but instead teach students how to argue either side of any proposition—the hired-gun approach to justice.

And in the midst of this sea of uncertainty, our culture yearns for someone to speak the truth with authority—the same mission given to us by Christ Himself. He wants us to speak with conviction, the way He spoke. Not in a judgmental way—"I judge no one" (John 8:15)—but in a way that combines hard-hitting truth with relentless love.

When we speak with conviction about Jesus, we become more like Him, not less. When we water down and soft sell and shuffle our feet as if we're embarrassed when we talk about Him, trying not to offend anyone with our firm religious convictions, then we send the signal that, like so many in our society, we really have nothing important to say. What an offense to the great message of salvation!

HAVE I GOT A QUESTION FOR YOU

The confrontation continued.

> Jesus answered them, "I will also ask you one question, and if you answer it for Me, then I will tell you by what authority I do these things. Where did John's baptism come from? From heaven or from men?"
>
> They began to argue among themselves, "If we say, 'From heaven,' He will say to us, 'Then why didn't you believe him?' But if we say, 'From men,' we're afraid of the crowd, because everyone thought John was a prophet." So they answered Jesus, "We don't know."
>
> And He said to them, "Neither will I tell you by what authority I do these things." (Matthew 21:24–27)

Imagine this! Jesus of Nazareth, the man who spoke with such authority that the temple police refused to arrest Him, now dodging a question about where that authority came from. Is this Freeborn John Lilburne stubbornly plugging his ears by this elaborate ploy of asking the Pharisees a question they can't answer? Is this God asserting His godly prerogative, making a point that He doesn't have to answer to these cynical religious leaders—"Where were you when I established the earth or laid its cornerstone?"

Probably. But there's more here as well. Keep in mind that Jesus had already stated in plain language where His authority came from. John wrote that Jesus literally "shouted to the crowds, 'If you trust me, you are really trusting God who sent me.... I don't speak on my own authority. The Father who sent me gave me his own instructions as to what I should say'" (John 12:44, 49, NLT). Of course, the religious leaders heard this. The trick here was whether they could get Christ to say it again *now*, so they could arrest Him for blasphemy here in Jerusalem, claiming that He put Himself on an equal footing with God.

Christ saw through their ploy. More than anything, His refusal to answer was a statement that He alone would choose the timing for His death. He had already reconciled Himself to the Cross, but first He would share a Passover meal with His disciples. "Not today," He was saying. "We're not going there yet."

But it wasn't just a matter of Jesus not being ready to answer yet. Those who asked the question clearly weren't ready to *hear* the answer either. John came preaching a message of repentance. Christ followed, preaching about the kingdom of God and His own authority. His point to the religious leaders was this: you must first embrace the repentance of John before you're ready for the authority of Christ.

It's a lesson we all need to learn. There are things God can't reveal to us because we're not yet ready for the answer. There are also things we will never understand, areas where we need to trust God based on results. Both of these were at play in this instance.

In addition, God has a bias on the side of action. "Don't just sit there and contemplate your navel," He says (Singer paraphrase, you understand), "driving yourself mad with all your whys and where-fores. Do something!"

God, why is there so much poverty in Africa? "Feed them!" God, why did innocent children lose their parents in the 2004 Asian tsunami? "Adopt them!" Why are the innocent accused? "Represent them!" Why are children abused? "Defend them!" What about my enemies, God—why do they prosper? "Love them!"

Our God is a Nike God. "Just do it!" He says. We'll figure it all out later.

Nearly a year after Bruce's death, I heard a pastor speak about the one thing we can do better on earth than we can in heaven. We will worship better in heaven, he said. We will fellowship better. We will understand more fully. But the one thing we can do better on earth is to tell others who are not yet Christ followers about the love and sacrifice of Jesus Christ. In a word, evangelism.

I put that in the context of my own experience. I still didn't know why God chose to take Bruce and leave me. But this much I knew—there is only one thing I can do better than Bruce right now, only one reason why God pulled me out of that whirlpool and gave me another day, another year, another three decades. And I made up my mind to try to do it with all my might.

AND THEN A PARABLE

It's no accident that Jesus, after refusing to answer the question of the religious leaders, illustrated His bias toward action with the following parable:

"A man had two sons. He went to the first and said, 'My son, go, work in the vineyard today.'

"He answered, 'I don't want to!' Yet later he changed his mind and went. Then the man went to the other and said the same thing.

" 'I will, sir,' he answered. But he didn't go.

"Which of the two did his father's will?"

"The first," they said.

Jesus said to them, "I assure you: Tax collectors and prostitutes are entering the kingdom of God before you!"

(Matthew 21:28–31)

The point is clear. God cares more about obedient actions than good intentions. He doesn't care whether we figure it all out. He wants us to follow His will, even if it doesn't make sense.

FAITH AND QUANTUM PHYSICS

"Faith," wrote the unnamed author of Hebrews, "is the substance of things hoped for, the evidence of things not seen" (Hebrews 11:1, NKJV). Every day of our lives, we put our faith in things we can't see and things we don't understand.

Who among us begins to understand the complexities of quantum physics (also known as quantum mechanics)? One of the leading thinkers in that bizarre frontier of science, Daniel Greenberger, a theorist at the City College of New York, describes it this way: "Einstein said that if quantum mechanics is right, then the world is crazy. Well, Einstein was right. The world is crazy."[4]

Crazy is an understatement. To a linear thinker like me, quantum physics resembles a world of fun-house mirrors, all doublespeak and nonsensical explanations that defy every rule of logic. Consider, for example, the two theories that physicists posit to explain how a single photon of light can apparently pass through two separate slits in a partition at the same time, thus creating a wavelike striped pattern measured on a screen on the other side of the partition.

One photon of light at a time is released...

...and creates a pattern of light and dark bands on a screen, indicating that each photon simultaneously passed through both slits, creating two wavelike patterns that interfered with each other.

The first theory is something called *superposition.* In this camp, scientists argue that if we don't know what a single particle of light is doing, we must assume that it is doing everything possible simultaneously.[5] Each possibility is a single physical state, and the photon of light is therefore said to be in superposition of state. We know that one photon left the filament, and we know that the same photon struck the screen on the other side of the partition. But in the meantime, we cannot measure its path, and so we must assume that the photon passed through both slits in the partition simultaneously. In other words, during the time when we couldn't observe this photon, it split into two ghost photons, which simultaneously went through both slits, creating the wavelike pattern of light on the other side.

If you think that sounds silly, consider the other camp. They explain this bizarre experiment by a concept called *multiverse*, meaning that whenever an object has the potential to enter one of several possible states, the universe splits into multiple universes, so that each potential is fulfilled in a separate universe. Thus, when the photon leaves the filament, it goes through one slit in one universe and one slit in another universe, then the two universes somehow interfere with each other on the other side of the partition, creating the wavelike striped pattern mentioned earlier.

I'm not making this stuff up.

Now, if you understand the ins and outs of quantum physics, you can skip to the next chapter, because this illustration won't work for you. But if you're like me and you're in that 99.9 percent who are starting to get a headache right about now, consider for a moment how important quantum physics is to our world. Without it, physicists couldn't calculate nuclear reactions in power stations, determine the intensity of the sun, or design the lasers we use for our CD players.[6]

In this crazy world, we use quantum physics every day, though the theories seem to defy common sense, because we know we can trust the results. When that single photon hits the screen on the other side of the partition, making a pattern that can be explained only if we assume that the photon existed in two places at once, or two universes at once, then we have to take that conclusion at face value. We learn to trust "the evidence of things unseen."

And so it is with God. God is the "true light" (John 1:9) and, like the single photon mentioned above, He is both superimposed (theologians call it omnipresent) and multiverse (existing both in this world and in a spiritual dimension). He may not always make sense to us—in fact, He may not usually make sense to us—but we can trust the results. We see evidence of His creative power all around us, from the magnitude of the universe to the complexities of a single photon of light. We see His redemptive work in the story of humankind. And we experience His transformational power in our own lives.

These are all the evidences of things unseen, the striped pattern of light that proves something miraculous exists beyond this world. Physicists believe it and call it science. We believe it and call it faith.

But the religious leaders of Christ's day wanted something more substantial. They wanted something they could touch and feel. None of this superposition or multiversing nonsense for them. "Who gave You this authority?" they challenged. But Christ refused to answer, choosing instead to pelt them with parables that predicted their demise. When they heard His parables, they looked for a way to arrest Him but feared the crowds, because the crowds regarded Christ as a prophet (see Matthew 21:45–46).

Christ's silence and popularity served Him well, allowing Him to delay His sacrifice until a few days later—until the appointed time. Then He would stand silent again, though this time the crowd would turn against Him. Even as they screamed for His execution, Christ would refuse to defend Himself. There are a few things in life more important than speaking in your own defense, even if you are innocent.

Freeborn John Lilburne could have told you that.

8

MAKING HEADS AND TAILS
OF CHURCH AND STATE

The Pharisees and lawyers were getting smart. At first they had underestimated Christ, no doubt about that. This Galilean, this son of a carpenter, had proved more formidable than they thought. Every off-the-cuff question backfired. He had stepped into their intellectual traps and emerged unscathed. The more He flouted their authority, the more His popularity grew.

They had started by confronting the issues head-on. He claimed to be forgiving sins—that was blasphemy! But when they called His hand, He performed miracles that won over the crowds. Jesus was no demagogue—He backed up words with actions.

They had argued late into the night about who was to blame for their own miscues and Jesus's growing popularity. The man could perform miracles. So why give Him a platform to help Him show off in front of large crowds? It was time to get more subtle. Time to use His own tendencies against Him.

Though He had dodged every one of their carefully crafted questions, it only increased their resolve. Like mosquitoes who survive the summer's insecticides, they would come back stronger. Wiser. At once more cautious and more daring.

They would not underestimate Him again. This time they would use His own words against Him. They would exploit His strengths, not attack His weaknesses. They would flatter Him first, setting up the knockout punch by reminding the crowd how Christ did not kowtow to any man. They would smoke out His political agenda. He might be willing to take on the Pharisees, but was He ready to take on the mighty Roman Empire?

Oh yes, and this time they would send someone else to do the dirty work. After all, they didn't want Him writing about them in the dirt again.

> Then the Pharisees went and plotted how to trap Him by what He said. They sent their disciples to Him, with the Herodians. "Teacher," they said, "we know that You are truthful and teach truthfully the way of God. You defer to no one, for You don't show partiality. Tell us, therefore, what You think. Is it lawful to pay taxes to Caesar or not?" (Matthew 22:15–17)

THE CORRUPT ROMAN EMPIRE

To the Jews, ancient Rome was a loathsome beast. Before the time of Christ, the Roman Empire had reached its zenith, the period historians refer to as the Pax Romana, or Roman peace. The great Augustus had reunited the empire following the civil wars triggered by the assassination of Julius Caesar. Tiberius followed Augustus, starting his reign with prudence and reform. But by the time of Christ's ministry, he had fled to the island of Capri in self-imposed exile, engaging in all kinds of sexual debauchery. He left the running of the empire to Sejanus, the head of the Praetorian Guard, a ruthless and cunning administrator who poisoned Tiberius's only son and then carried on an affair with the son's widow.

Despite this dysfunctional leadership, the empire still flourished. Roman legions assured the peace while citizens enjoyed a combination of Roman justice, Greek culture, and barbaric entertainment. Even the conquered peoples recognized the benefits of Roman rule and the wisdom of the great Caesar.

Except in Palestine.

The Jews refused to abandon their worship of the One True God in order to accommodate the many gods of Rome. They chafed at worshiping the emperor. The Romans thought them atheists, and Sejanus expelled them from Rome.

Then, at the height of Sejanus's power, Tiberius caught wind of a treasonous plot and had Sejanus executed. A time of paranoia followed, with torture and treason trials resulting in the deaths of anyone suspected of opposing Tiberius. Men, women, and children met their deaths based on trumped-up charges. Because of a law forbidding the beheading of virgins, Tiberius would routinely have the executioners rape the young women before killing them. One man was executed for having the audacity to take a coin bearing the image of Tiberius into the public bathroom with him. Paranoia and terror reigned.

In Palestine, Pontius Pilate served as the Roman procurator and Herod Antipas reigned as the Jewish tetrarch with the blessing of Rome. The Jews hated both. Unscrupulous Jewish tax collectors working for Rome were paid a percentage of what they could coerce from their fellow citizens. Though Tiberius had reduced luxury expenses in Rome, providing the provinces with a tax cut, the thought of supporting the pagan Roman lifestyle through an unfair collection system still grated on the Jews.

The long-awaited Jewish Messiah would break the Roman yoke. The Jews prayed desperately for His coming. Devout Jews would set aside an empty seat for the Messiah each day at the evening meal. Like the second coming of Moses, the Messiah would free the Israelites from bondage and demonstrate anew the power of Yahweh. He would restore the Davidic kingdom, a kingdom that God Himself had promised would never end.

For the average Jew, it couldn't happen fast enough. They had suffered for hundreds of years under foreign occupation and had watched false messiahs come and go. They had seen their hopes raised and dashed, with each new revolt by the latest pseudo-Messiah bringing more oppression than before.

But Jesus was different. He confounded the religious leaders. No one had ever taught with such authority! He produced a miracle a minute. Impressive stuff too. Things that had never been done before. And He made no bones about being the long-awaited Messiah.

Like the time He read Scripture in the temple. He opened the scrolls to a passage from Isaiah that everyone knew referred to the Messiah:

The Spirit of the Lord is on Me,
because He has anointed Me
to preach good news to the poor.
He has sent Me
to proclaim freedom to the captives
and recovery of sight to the blind,
to set free the oppressed,
to proclaim the year of the Lord's favor. (Luke 4:18–19)

Then Christ sat down and waited until all eyes were fixed on Him. "Today as you listen, this Scripture has been fulfilled," He said (verse 21).

So, what was He waiting for?

The zealous Jews, the ones who acknowledged no king but God, were more than ready. It wasn't a matter of raising a large army. If every Jew took up arms, they would still be no match for the legions of Rome. But this would be supernatural—the ten plagues Moses brought down on Egypt would look like child's play. For once, it would be the Romans who would suffer.

The Pharisees wanted to smoke Jesus out for entirely different reasons. Like the zealots, they had no doubt that He would one day take on Rome. When He did, He would be quashed like the imposter they knew Him to be. But in the meantime, Christ's popularity increased while theirs disintegrated. It was time to force His hand.

The hated Roman tax would be their vehicle of choice. No self-proclaimed Messiah could support this oppressive tax, used to finance the lavish lifestyles and pagan practices of Roman aristocrats. To rub salt in the wound, the Romans insisted that it be paid with the silver denarius, a coin that contained an image of Tiberius Caesar and this inscription: *Tiberius Caesar Augustus, Son of the Divine Augustus.* The reverse side contained the words *Chief Priest,* another title for Tiberius. Even using the coin was viewed by many Jews as an act of idolatry and sacrilege, acknowledging Caesar as both god and chief priest.

It was no wonder that many would-be messiahs took their stand on this issue. The Pharisees thought it would make the perfect trap. Christ had proved slippery before, but how could He wiggle out of this one?

"Tell us, therefore, what You think. Is it lawful to pay taxes to Caesar or not?"

If Christ said yes, His popularity would plummet. The fiery revolutionary would be exposed as the doormat of Rome. If He said no... well, that's why the Herodians went along. They would seize Him immediately, and He would never be heard from again—another footnote in the Roman domination of Palestine.[1]

MY KINGDOM IS NOT OF THIS WORLD

Perceiving their malice, Jesus said, "Why are you testing Me, hypocrites? Show Me the coin used for the tax." So they brought Him a denarius. "Whose image and inscription is this?" He asked them.

"Caesar's," they said to Him.

Then He said to them, "Therefore, give back to Caesar

the things that are Caesar's, and to God the things that are
God's." When they heard this, they were amazed. So they left
Him and went away. (Matthew 22:18–22)

Two thousand years later, we still struggle with the profundity of
this answer. Like the zealots, some want political dominance, as if the
kingdom of Christ can be ushered in at the ballot box. On the other
extreme are those who ignore the second part of Christ's answer, as if
it were just a nice phrase used to round out the poetic symmetry of
His response. They miss the sweeping implications of this gratuitous
comment—render unto God the things that are God's. As we will
soon see, this part of His answer means, quite literally, everything.

CHRIST IS NOT A CONSERVATIVE

Or a liberal. Or a Republican. Or a Democrat.

No political party or ideology can contain Him, because Jesus is
above politics. That's what prompted the first part of His response.
But He longs for godly politicians. Our faith should influence everything we do, every corner of God's creation, including that dirty little
corner called politics. And that's why He included the second part of
His response.

With two thousand years of Christian history at our back, the wisdom of Jesus's answer is more apparent than ever. We've seen His
redemptive plan unfold. We realize that He didn't come just to deliver
one nation at one moment in history from the chains of bondage. He
came to deliver all mankind for all time. Oppressed people everywhere

still take refuge in the freedom He provides. He came to deliver from sin, not from Roman imperialism. He came to set us free from the chains that matter most.

To do that, the Romans and the Sanhedrin had to win round one. A horrific death on the cross was the battle plan. Our deliverance depended on Christ's subjugation; our freedom depended on His humiliation.

But the answer is not quite that easy. After the Resurrection, Christ could have led a popular revolt against a corrupt Roman government. He could have been both the Savior of our souls and the deliverer of the Jewish nation. After all, God cares about justice and abhors nations who oppress the weak. Why, then, did Christ choose not to become involved politically? Didn't He know that Tiberius would soon be replaced by the madman Nero? Didn't He foresee that, within thirty years, Nero would light the streets of Rome with burning Christians? Why didn't Christ stop this chain of events and help enthrone a benevolent leader as Caesar?

Nearly three hundred years later, in a sense, He did. The dramatic conversion of Emperor Constantine, and the adoption of Christianity throughout the Roman Empire, is further proof of the wisdom of Christ's response to the Pharisees. Though Christianity had flourished as a persecuted sect in the years prior to Constantine, the rise of Christians to positions of great power had a corrupting effect on the church. Instead of the church sanctifying the state, the state scandalized the church.

It would be a pattern repeated throughout history, across cultural and political lines. A state-sponsored church is a weak and corrupt church. Christianity works best when its people are a remnant, a pure and unadulterated religious group that nobody joins for ulterior purposes.

Jesus also knew that conversion is authentic only when it's voluntary. Nobody can be coerced into accepting Jesus, nor can morals be legislated in a meaningful way. At best, government acts as a restraint on its citizens. But real change comes from within—the kingdom of the heart.

We would do well to remember this in twenty-first-century America. It seems that one of the favorite pastimes of Christians these days is to criticize our nation's judiciary. They are an easy target, with rulings protecting abortion, removing prayer from public schools, and legitimizing gay marriage. We spend a lot of energy ensuring the selection of conservative judges to the bench—judges who believe in a strict interpretation of our Constitution and the ideals of our Founding Fathers.

And well we should.

But this is merely a rearguard action, an incremental battle we are destined to lose. It's like the game at the amusement park where plastic frogs pop up and you hit them over the head with a plastic hammer. The faster you hammer, the faster the frogs pop up. Great exercise, but you aren't making much progress.

Our greatest energy and our grandest hope must focus on penetrating the political arena and the legal profession with the gospel of Jesus Christ. Only Christ can create new creatures—Christian lawyers and politicians and judges—with a whole new outlook on life. If we take care of the spiritual battle, the political battle will take care of itself.

Just ask Herb Titus.

Formerly an ACLU cooperating attorney and an ultraliberal law-school professor, Herb wasn't afraid of unpopular causes—like helping draft dodgers stay out of the Vietnam War. He belittled anything to do with Christianity, including the trembling law student who made an appointment with him for the purpose of sharing Christ. Professor Titus sloughed off the student's Christian testimony, dismissing it with the thought that he was only a C student who therefore needed Jesus.

But a seed had been planted, and within a few months, God caused a completely unforeseeable turnaround. In an attempt to save his failing marriage, Herb finally agreed to go to church with his wife, Marilyn. After they picked a church out of the newspaper, they found themselves in a Sunday-school class where the teacher literally recited their private conversations from two nights before, using the same words, asking the same questions about their lives, but with one difference—the teacher gave answers to those questions from the Bible. "At first we thought it was just a coincidence," Herb recalled, "but the Word of God penetrated our very beings, dividing our souls and spirits and the thoughts and intentions of our hearts, just like it says in Hebrews 4:12."

At the end of the class, Herb and Marilyn both gave their lives to Christ. "We were so excited," said Herb. "We ended up in the church parking lot laughing and crying and trying to understand what had just happened to us. And then it dawned on us. 'Hey, we left our boys in the church.' So we rushed back in, retrieved our boys, and within twenty-four hours, God gave us a brand-new marriage and family life."

Recently, I had a chance to team teach a seminar for Christian law students with Herb. After Herb gave his testimony, one of the students asked how that conversion experience changed his view of the law.

Herb laughed. "It changed everything," he said. "I started looking at God's Word as the ultimate law and realized that all justice flows from Him." From an ACLU lawyer to a stint as dean of a Christian law school, from defending draft dodgers to defending Judge Roy Moore, the "Ten Commandments judge," Herb isn't kidding when he says Jesus changed everything.

There are plenty of Christians intent on changing our nation's laws. But there aren't many, like that scared law student from the University of Oregon, intent on changing the hearts of our nation's lawyers. Christ didn't lead a political revolt, but He did try to convert the rich young ruler. He never led an army, but He did heal the centurion's daughter. He didn't try to reform the Sanhedrin, but He did meet with Nicodemus, a member of the Sanhedrin, at night.

"Give back to Caesar the things that are Caesar's," He said. But He didn't stop there.

RENDERING UNTO GOD

Jesus finished His answer by urging His interrogators "to [give] God the things that are God's." This is not His way of sanctioning some type of *Time* magazine life: you've got a political part of your life, a lifestyle section, a culture section, and a religion section—and you should never let them intersect. Jesus is not suggesting that, like loyalty to Caesar, our loyalty to God is limited to certain aspects of life. Instead, He's contrasting the limited duty we owe Caesar with the unlimited duty we owe God.

"Whose image and inscription is [on the coin]?" He asked. And the obvious answer was "Caesar's." But whose inscription is on the earth and everything in it? This is the implied question in the second half of Christ's response. And His Jewish listeners knew the way the psalmist answered:

> The heavens are yours, and the earth is yours;
>> everything in the world is yours—you created it all.
>> (Psalm 89:11, NLT)

On this point Christ never varied: God wants all of our lives or nothing at all. Thus, when the rich ruler came to Christ, asking what he needed to do in order to inherit eternal life, Christ told him to sell *everything he had* and distribute the money to the poor (see Luke 18:22). And when an expert in the Law asked essentially the same question, Christ affirmed that the correct answer was to "Love the Lord your God with *all* your heart, with *all* your soul, with *all* your strength, and with *all* your mind; and your neighbor as yourself" (Luke 10:27, emphasis added). Then Jesus helped the expert understand what this meant by telling the story of the good Samaritan.

In other words, while politics should never influence our faith, our faith had better influence our politics.

For this reason, Jesus would have little patience with modern-day hard-core separatists—those who claim that there should be an impregnable wall between church and state. For them, politics and faith are two different jurisdictions, and nothing scares them more than a politician who claims to be motivated by religious thinking. It's a mind-set that permeates our universities and the intellectual elites who run them. In their view, nothing is more dangerous to a free society than a "religious fundamentalist."

Listen to the way Stephen Carter, a teacher at Yale Law School and a charter member of our nation's intelligentsia, describes this mind-set among his peers (notably, this quote comes from a chapter entitled "God as a Hobby"):

One good way to end a conversation—or start an argument—is to tell a group of well-educated professionals that you hold a political position (preferably a controversial one, such as being against abortion or pornography) because it is required by your understanding of God's will. In the unlikely event that anyone hangs around to talk with you about it, the chances are that you will be challenged on the ground that you are intent on imposing your religious beliefs on other people. And in contemporary political and legal culture, nothing is worse.

That awful phrase—"imposing religious beliefs"—conjures up images of the religious right, the Reverend Jerry Falwell's Moral Majority, the Reverend Pat Robertson's presidential campaign, the 1992 Republican Convention, and the rest comes out in a jumble of post-Enlightenment angst: We live in a *secular* culture devoted to sweet reason. We separate church and state. We believe in tolerance. We aren't superstitious. Taking religion seriously is something only those wild-eyed zealots do: Operation Rescue, blocking the entrances to abortion clinics...you know who I mean, those Christian fundamentalists...the evangelicals...the folks who want class-room prayer in public school, but think that God doesn't hear the prayers of Jews...you know, those television preachers... those snake-charming faith healers...and the "scientific" creationists...*Southern Baptists,* for goodness sake!... Well, they're scary people.[2]

The truly scary thing is that this mind-set is found not only among secular humanists but among many mainline Christians as well. For support they cite the apolitical nature of Christ's ministry and the ideals of our Founding Fathers. But in reality, neither justifies their position.

Christ did not call the rich young ruler to withdraw from politics nor tell the centurion to leave his post. On the contrary, He praised the centurion, saying He had found no greater faith in all of Israel. Christ did not call us to separate but to permeate. If you rule, rule justly. If you legislate, pass laws wisely. When you vote, vote those issues that matter most to the heart of God.

Christ was a defender of children:

Whoever causes the downfall of one of these little ones who believe in Me—it would be better for him if a heavy millstone were hung around his neck and he were drowned in the depths of the sea! Woe to the world because of offenses. For offenses must come, but woe to that man by whom the offense comes. (Matthew 18:6–7)

And He was an uncompromising advocate of social justice:

I was hungry
and you gave Me nothing to eat;
I was thirsty
and you gave Me nothing to drink;
I was a stranger
and you didn't take Me in;
I was naked
and you didn't clothe Me,
sick and in prison
and you didn't take care of Me....

I assure you: Whatever you did not do for one of the least
of these, you did not do for Me either. (Matthew 25:42–43, 45)

Do we really think Christ doesn't care about issues like abortion
and poverty? Do we really think the man who spent His life protecting the poor, the helpless, and the disenfranchised (and who is more
helpless than a child in the womb?)—would just turn His back on
public-policy issues affecting them?

"Give...to God the things that are God's," Christ admonished.
And this includes *everything*.

THE FAITH OF OUR FOUNDING FATHERS

Our Founding Fathers firmly believed that every ruler was subject to
God's authority. They would have scoffed at the modern notion of
a complete separation between faith and politics. They would be
shocked to know that supporters of that notion cite the Founding
Fathers themselves as justification.

If they believed anything, they believed that their revolutionary actions were justified—no, even more, *required*—by the Creator who endowed them with certain inalienable rights. Far from separating God from politics, they believed that God's Law demanded drastic political action—political independence, a course certain to require a high price in human lives.

In his essay "In Defense of Certainty," Charles Krauthammer vividly describes how far the current strand of secular thinking has drifted from the religious mind-set of the nation's founders:

The Op-Ed pages are filled with jeremiads about believers—principally evangelical Christians and traditional Catholics—bent on turning the U.S. into a theocracy. Now I am not much of a believer, but there is something deeply wrong—indeed, deeply un-American—about fearing people simply because they believe. It seems perfectly okay for secularists to impose their secular views on America, such as, say, legalized abortion or gay marriage. But when someone takes a contrary view...rooted in Scripture or some kind of religious belief system, the very public advocacy of that view becomes a violation of the U.S. constitutional order.

What nonsense.... You want religiosity? How about a people who overthrow the political order of the ages, go to war and occasion thousands of deaths in the name of self-evident truths and unalienable rights endowed by the Creator? That was 1776. The universality, the sacredness and the divine origin of freedom are enshrined in our founding document. The Founders, believers all, signed it. Thomas Jefferson wrote it.

And not even Jefferson, the most skeptical of the lot, had the slightest doubt about it.[3]

Ironic, isn't it? Jefferson, the man who penned the words "wall of separation" in a letter to the Danbury Baptist Association (a phrase, by the way, that is found nowhere in our Constitution), is the same man who justified our country's independence by reference to our Creator and His divine order. You can mark Jefferson's words in the Declaration of Independence—an exercise that will generate no fewer than four independent references to God. And the primary basis for our revolt? Unfair taxation. The same issue that Christ refused to take a stand on two thousand years ago.

Was this a repudiation of Christ's teaching by Jefferson and our Founding Fathers? Or a proper understanding of what it means to give God all things—even those things that fall into the realm of the political? Maybe especially those things.

"My mission is not to start a tax revolt," Christ explained, "but everything, including the rulers whom God has allowed to rule, is subject to His authority and should govern by His principles. God is not a zealot or a collaborator," Christ was saying. "He does not come to take sides. He comes to take over."

"When they heard this, they were amazed. So they left Him and went away" (Matthew 22:22).

9

THE WITNESS STRIKES BACK

The problem with Jesus is that He's not good at sharing. The Christian faith would be a whole lot less controversial if He were just one of many gods—or, better yet, one of many prophets. Those outside the faith could follow some of His teachings and reject others. Christians wouldn't have to sound and feel so close-minded and judgmental. Life would be the way it was described in a *U.S. News and World Report* cover story on faith in America, where the author quoted a woman from Tennessee: "Say God is Nashville. Some people are going to take I-40 East and others will take I-40 West, depending on where they're coming from."[1]

Quaint, but not the way Jesus viewed it. "I am *the* way, *the* truth, and *the* life," He said. "No one comes to the Father except through Me" (John 14:6, emphasis added).

Our God "is a jealous God" (Exodus 34:14, NIV). And Jesus is an exclusive Savior. It's what causes so much consternation today, and it's the same issue that generated heat during the final days of Jesus's ministry. He wasn't willing to take a place among the other prophets, one brand out of many, take your choice. Instead, He insisted that some-day all of creation would become His footstool.

With tensions running high in Jerusalem, and with the Passover only days away, the Pharisees and lawyers made one final run at dis-crediting Jesus. It would be their last public effort, one that would fail miserably and force them into a secret conspiracy with Judas. It would be an embarrassing confrontation for the religious leaders—turning the witness into the prosecutor.

At the end of the confrontation, Matthew would sum it up this way: "From that day no one dared to question Him any more" (Matthew 22:46).

It started when the arch rivals in the religious establishment—the Pharisees and the Sadducees—came together, fueled by their common hatred for Christ. The man had just silenced the Sadducees by answering a convoluted question about heaven (if seven brothers die in succession, each having been married to the same woman, whose wife will she be in the resurrection?) with reasoning that "astonished" the crowd (see Matthew 22:33). As the Sadducees were licking their wounds, they found kindred spirits in their traditional adversaries. "When the Pharisees heard that He had silenced the Sadducees, they came together in the same place. And one of them, an expert in the law, asked a question to test Him: 'Teacher, which commandment in the law is the greatest?' " (verses 34–36).

Before we hear Christ's straightforward answer, we need to under-stand why the question was asked in the first place. The lawyer asked the question as a "test," Scripture says. He probably wanted to force Jesus to pick one particular area of the Law because He knew that this would automatically alienate all the other religious leaders who specialized in a competing area of the Law.

Think of it as a gathering of legal specialists, all trying to demonstrate that their area of the Law was more important than the other specialties. These religious leaders had developed a nearly indecipherable web of laws and traditions—thousands of them, with specialties and subspecialties governing conduct as obscure as how many steps you could walk on the Sabbath before walking would be considered work. All of these laws, of course, justified the existence of numerous experts in the Law Pharisees, Sadducees, scribes, and lawyers, all fervent defenders of their own area of expertise and debaters of every esoteric act that their specialty governed. This guy specialized in Sabbath observances; this one could tell you all about blemishes on animals used for sacrifices; another one loved to talk about circumcision. It was almost as if Christ were surrounded by a convention of tax lawyers, each a specialist in a little-known part of the IRS code, and now He had to pronounce the most important part of the code.

Except the passions at play were considerably higher. Maybe more like a gang of rabid football fans, all from different cities, and you've been asked to pick your favorite. I'm a Packers fan, you announce. One enlightened man cheers and thirty-five others boo. The Steelers fan wants to call you out. Not exactly the best way to increase your popularity.

But Christ doesn't even blink at the question. "Love the Lord your God with all your heart, with all your soul, and with all your mind. This is the greatest and most important commandment. The second is like it: Love your neighbor as yourself. All the Law and the Prophets depend on these two commandments" (Matthew 22:37–40).

In these few plain sentences, the Master Teacher summarizes the entire Law of Moses. Indeed, the crux of all Scripture, both the Law *and* the Prophets. His answer is so straightforward, so plain and self-explanatory, that a child can understand it. Love is the verb. God is the object. Our neighbor is the beneficiary. The beautiful simplicity of Christ's response touches even the lawyer who asked the question.

"You are right, Teacher!" the lawyer cries out (Mark 12:32).[2] Imagine the surprised looks on the faces of the other religious leaders. For the first time in nearly three years of cross-examination, a questioner has conceded defeat!

You can almost feel this lawyer's excitement as he restates Christ's magnificent answer (being a lawyer, he just had to reword it a little). The scales drop from his eyes as the big picture zooms into view: "You have correctly said that He is One, and there is no one else except Him. And to love Him with all your heart, with all your understanding, and with all your strength, and to love your neighbor as yourself, is far more important than all the burnt offerings and sacrifices" (Mark 12:32–33).

And Jesus, sensing the man's sincerity, responds in kind: "You are not far from the kingdom of God" (Mark 12:34).

Wait a minute! "Not far" from the kingdom? What does Jesus mean by "not far"? What else can this poor guy do? He asks Jesus for the greatest commandment, and Jesus tells him. Persuaded, this man agrees with Jesus, regurgitating the very answer that Jesus just articulated seconds before. But still Jesus implies that this lawyer is not quite there. "Not far," Jesus says.

Maybe I'm overanalyzing this, but I know exactly how this lawyer felt. I can still picture sitting in my mentor's office, a few months out of law school, discussing a responsive pleading I had drafted to a civil lawsuit. Drafting responsive pleadings is not hard; you just deny as much as you can about what the other side is claiming and make sure you add the appropriate affirmative defenses. I would later be able to do them in my sleep, but at the time I was struggling. You see, it's not something you spend much time on in law school, and I had an exacting mentor who wanted me to learn everything he knew. For my part, I wanted to impress. But that wasn't happening.

If I recall correctly, this was my third time in his office on this same pleading. The first time I hadn't denied enough of the allegations. The second time I had forgotten to add a few rather far-fetched affirmative defenses. I didn't include them because I didn't think we could prove them. But my mentor argued that you never knew what would happen during the case, and if we didn't at least mention them at this stage, we would be precluded from raising them at trial.

Fine. I put them in. But a few days later, we were looking at the same pleading for the third time and now my mentor was shaking his head again. "Why'd you put this defense in?" he asked. "We'll never be able to prove this one at trial."

At first I thought he was kidding, but his frown soon changed my mind. "Because you told me to?"

His brow furrowed deeper, but the frown never left. The red pen came out, and he scratched through the defense. "I never said I'd be consistent," he mumbled.

Is that what's happening here with Christ? Inconsistency? "I'll tell you the most important commandments," Christ says. And when the lawyer repeats them back, the very same commandments, he gets a B plus. "Not bad," says Christ. "Not far."

What was the lawyer missing?

CHRIST'S RIDDLE

The lawyer understood his duty to love God and his neighbor, but he didn't yet fully grasp the role of Jesus the Messiah. It was a concept Jesus would explain by using a riddle.

> While the Pharisees were together, Jesus questioned them,
> "What do you think about the Messiah? Whose Son is He?"
>   "David's," they told Him.
>   He asked them, "How is it then that David, inspired by
> the Spirit, calls Him 'Lord':
>   The Lord declared to my Lord,
>   'Sit at My right hand
>   until I put Your enemies under Your feet'?
>   "If David calls Him 'Lord,' how then can the Messiah be
> his Son?" No one was able to answer Him at all, and from
> that day no one dared to question Him any more. (Matthew
> 22:41–46)

Note that the first thing Christ did, like any good lawyer, was to ask the classic setup question. "Whose Son is the Messiah?" An easy question. A gimme. The Pharisees knew that the Scriptures were abundantly plain on this point. The Messiah would be of the lineage of David and would reign with righteousness on the throne of David forever.[3] It's why Matthew began his gospel with a genealogy that demonstrates, among other things, that Christ was a descendant of David. The required bloodline for the Messiah was beyond dispute.

But then Christ took them to an ancient and sacred text written by David that refers to this same Messiah. Quoting Psalm 110:1, Christ asked why David would call his own descendant "Lord." This may not seem much like a quandary to us, but in the first-century Jewish culture, where the older generations were revered, it would be unheard of for a patriarch like David to call one of his own descendants by the exalted title of Lord.

Picture this austere collection of scribes and Pharisees furrowing their brows, shaking their heads, shuffling their feet, gently nudging one another to step up and answer the man's question. It couldn't have been the first time they had ever thought about this troubling passage. These men knew Scripture backward and forward. But in all their years of study and debate, nobody had come up with a satisfactory explanation for this conundrum Jesus had just raised. And maybe the question that troubled them even more was this—how did He know their Achilles heel? And how many other passages of Scripture, just like this one, did He have up His sleeve?

Suddenly, Jesus had raised the stakes in this cross-examination battle. Was He now going on the offensive, not just answering questions but asking them as well? Would He skewer them with their own Scripture, laying bare the logical flaws in their strained interpretations? Perhaps this is why, from that day forward, nobody dared asked Him any more questions.

CHRIST'S MO

This was classic Christ—His modus operandi for apologetics. Scripture and common sense. Quote the black and white of Scripture but use your gray matter, too. The greatest commandment, according to Jesus, includes loving God with all our mind. But dependence on our own intellect, unanchored in scriptural truth, makes us like the secular philosophers of Christ's day—the Stoics and Epicureans. All these world-views proved inadequate when confronted with the teachings of Christ.

Many tend to see the intellectual approach and the biblical approach as contradictory rather than complementary. And while the pendulum tends to swing on this, right now the church seems more concerned with reliance on a logical apologetic than a biblical one. We live in a post-Christian society, the argument goes. The Bible is no longer viewed as authoritative. Many in our society, perhaps most, have never even read the Bible anyway. We've got to start where they are—appeal to their common sense and logic, their own sense of morals. When you start quoting Scripture, they will just turn you off.

There is some merit to this, of course, and far too often we try to answer every intellectual objection to our faith with a Scripture verse and nothing else. Some Christians who claim to believe in the inerrancy of Scripture don't even know how the books of Scripture were chosen. Many have never read the holy books of other religions or studied the beliefs of other faiths. Some cannot construct a single argument for the existence of God or His attributes apart from Scripture.

Yet Paul reminds us that "from the creation of the world His invisible attributes, that is, His eternal power and divine nature, have been clearly seen, being understood through what He has made" (Romans 1:20). Is not all truth God's truth? Everything we know about this world, including man's unique moral and spiritual nature, testifies to the truth of Scripture. Why should we be afraid to engage those who think differently than we do?

Paul had no such fears. Though he didn't possess "brilliance of speech or wisdom," he traveled to Mars Hill and debated the foremost philosophers of his day. (Some ridiculed him, but others believed; see 1 Corinthians 2:1; Acts 17:32–34). Christ had no such fears. As we've seen, His entire ministry was riddled with confrontations and hostile questions. And He didn't often win over His questioners.

Likewise, we should be prepared to engage the skeptics of our age. Scripture contains all that is necessary to live and understand our faith. But this does not require that we shun the study of great thinkers and provocative writers. We should know what those outside our faith believe. We should listen earnestly to their hearts (as opposed to just looking for a weakness in their belief system to hammer). We should not be concerned with whether we "win" arguments. Our job is to speak truth. Once it's out there, the truth will take care of itself.

We cannot, however, leave Scripture behind in the process. When did the recorded words of Christ become irrelevant to the pursuit of truth? The greatest teacher and philosopher of all time suddenly has nothing to say that our society needs to hear? This man's teachings, which once had the power to transform millions, have now become impotent? What Christian would dare say that his or her own arguments carry more weight than the arguments of Jesus or those of great apologists like the apostle Paul?

"But others won't listen to us if we appeal to Scripture," we fret. If we believe that, our words become a self-fulfilling prophecy. Our tepid defense of Scripture makes those outside the church wary of it. Why should they believe in something that we seem inclined to hide behind our backs?

LENIN, MARVIN, AND A RUSSIAN BIBLE

A few years ago, I coauthored a book entitled *Made to Count*, the story of God's using men and women who are not in traditional ministry roles. One of the people I interviewed for that book was a man named Marvin Olasky, a University of Texas journalism professor who presently serves as editor in chief of *World* magazine. *World* is America's fourth-largest weekly magazine, and unlike its competitors, it looks at current events from a biblical perspective.

Which would come as quite a shock for anybody who knew Marvin Olasky as a young man.

He grew up in a Jewish family in New England and, he says, "followed the sad tradition of contemporary Judaism: Bar mitzvah at thirteen; atheist at fourteen."[4] By college, Olasky had learned to question authority and espouse radical leftist ideas. "What I remember most about college is that I could do and write the silliest things and receive plaudits, as long as my lunacy was leftward." After he graduated, the young socialist officially joined the Communist Party, using journalism to advance his ideas.

I had it all figured out intellectually. There was no God who could change people from the inside out, and ordinary individuals were unimportant anyway. Radical change could come only from the outside in…through dictatorial action by a wise collection of leaders who would act for the good of all—and I would be one of those leaders.

Eventually, Olasky landed in graduate school at the University of Michigan. It was there that he first began doubting his world-view. Those doubts, ironically enough, were triggered when Olasky reread Lenin's famous essay "Socialism and Religion." Olasky comments, "At that point God changed my world-view not through thunder or a whirlwind, but by means of a small whisper that became a repeated, resounding question in my brain: *What if Lenin is wrong? What if there is a God?*"

Nearly a year later, Olasky was required to develop a reading knowledge of Russian for his doctoral program. He wanted to practice immediately, but the only thing handy in his apartment was a Russian New Testament that had been given to him as a novelty item a few years before. He plucked it from his bookcase and began reading. "To my surprise, what had seemed like superstition now had the ring of truth." The next year, Olasky was assigned to teach a course in early American literature, heavy in Puritan sermons. "Those dead white males also made great sense to me."

Two years later, Olasky would give his life to Christ. "Reading the whole Bible helped me to confess sin, because apart from the New Testament, neither the full gravity of man's problem nor the full opportunity for redemption is clear." Eventually, God would use

Professor Olasky to help focus Christians on the plight of the poor. He set a personal example, helping to set up New Start and City School (faith-based antipoverty and educational programs), helping his wife with a crisis pregnancy center, and adopting a three-week-old, at-risk African American baby. He also advocated a new kind of conservative compassion, which eventually formed the philosophy behind many of the programs implemented by President George W. Bush.

But it all started with an untutored reading of a Russian New Testament. Olasky had nobody there to explain or defend the words of Scripture, yet still he recognized that it had the "ring of truth."

SHARPENING OUR SWORD

"The word of God is living and effective and sharper than any two-edged sword, penetrating as far as to divide soul, spirit, joints, and marrow; it is a judge of the ideas and thoughts of the heart" (Hebrews 4:12). When we back away from Scripture, we are like an ancient warrior heading into battle but leaving behind his sword. We might be able to fend off a few blows with the shield of our logic, but at the end of the day, we'll still feel pretty powerless.

Jesus never dreamed of doing such a thing.

When Satan confronted Jesus in the wilderness, Jesus quoted Scripture. When Jesus taught in the temple complex, He quoted Scripture. When He debated the scribes and Pharisees, He used Scripture. At His trial in front of the Sanhedrin, the few words He spoke included quotes from Psalms and Daniel. And when He hung on the cross, His very groanings—"My God, My God, why have You forsaken me?"—were direct quotes from a psalm of David.[5]

You get the idea. Jesus was a big fan of Scripture. Mull that over. The Savior of the world, the Son of God whose very words would become Scripture themselves, time and again referred to the words of the Old Testament for guidance, authority, and comfort. And in the confrontation we're studying, while debating with the Pharisees, He affirmed that the words of David were "inspired by the Spirit" (Matthew 22:43); they were not just wise counsel from the flesh.

Several years ago my mother was staying at our home for a few days. During that time I noticed that she was working intensely to memorize some verses of Scripture. At the time she was nearing retirement age (I am prohibited under pain of grounding from revealing the exact years—hey, she's still my mom), and she was working with my aunt (nearly eighty years old) on Scripture memory. *Impressive,* I thought. *I'm glad they're keeping their minds sharp.* I asked her what verses she was memorizing.

"The book of James," she said.

That shamed me into my own Bible memory program. My competitive instincts kicked in. If my mother and aunt could memorize the book of James, then I could memorize James and Ephesians. Maybe throw in Jude, for that matter. What started as a result of pride (admittedly, not the best motivation, but by chapter 4, James had taken care of that—"God resists the proud, but gives grace to the humble") soon became a life-changing experience. When your memory is as weak as mine, you have to spend a lot of time saying the words over and over, and it does something to you. They become a part of you.

They were a part of Christ.

In the last few years, I've been doing informal surveys when I speak to large groups. Many times I'll ask people who have been Christ followers for more than five years to stand up. Then I'll ask people to remain standing if they can recite at least twenty verses of Scripture from heart—four verses for every year they've been a Christ follower. Typically, large numbers will stand for the first question. But then all but a few will sit when I ask the second one. (I then give a pop quiz, which sometimes causes a few more to sheepishly take their seat.)

How about you? Are you ready for the same pop quiz?

Are you a follower of Christ?

If so, for how many years have you been following Him?

Now, how many verses of Scripture have you memorized?

Do the math. How many verses per year have you learned?

Scripture and logic. This was the MO of Christ. It requires diligence and study. Being like Him means that we are always "ready to give a defense to anyone who asks [us] for a reason for the hope that is in [us]" (1 Peter 3:15). How can we do that if we know so little of God's Word?

SITTING AT GOD'S RIGHT HAND

Imagine David, a thousand years before the advent of Christ, writing the words of Psalm 110. David, an ardent believer in the monotheistic God of the Jewish faith. Yet he looks into heaven, inspired by the Holy Spirit, and writes down a scene incomprehensible even to him.

The LORD [the Hebrew word is *Yahweh*] declared to my Lord
[the Hebrew here is *Adonai,* understood as a reference to the
Messiah]:
"Sit at My right hand
until I make Your enemies Your footstool." (Psalm 110:1)

Here's what's so amazing about this: David referred to his own off-
spring, the anticipated Messiah, as Adonai.

Adonai is a word that typically implies deity. "My God [Elohim]
and my LORD [Adonai]," David cried on other occasions (Psalm
35:23; 38:15). In a vision, Isaiah saw himself standing in front of
God's throne and "heard the voice of [Adonai] saying: 'Who should
I send? Who will go for *Us?*'" (Isaiah 6:8, emphasis added). Daniel
called on the same name in repentance for the nation of Israel:
"[Adonai], hear! [Adonai], forgive! [Adonai], listen and act! My God,
for Your own sake, do not delay, because Your city and Your people
are called by Your name" (Daniel 9:19).

But in Psalm 110:1, David is plainly using the term *Adonai* as
something other than a reference to Yahweh. "The LORD [Yahweh]
declared to my Lord [Adonai]: 'Sit at My right hand…'" The scribes
and Pharisees all assumed that the word *Adonai* in this context was a
reference to the Messiah.

Still, the passage troubled them because they had always viewed
the Messiah as a future earthly political leader, a deliverer like Moses,
not some kind of co-regent with God. But here was David's psalm,
positioning the Messiah at the right hand of God, calling Him by a
name that implied deity.

Was this monotheism or something else?

Nobody could explain this psalm before the advent of Christ. Fully God and fully man, Jesus was both the son of David and co-regent with God the Father. Apart from Jesus, this scripture had no meaning. Illuminated by Jesus, its meaning became plain.

But not for the Pharisees. None of them was able to answer Him, Matthew said (see Matthew 22:46). Or maybe none of them dared. They knew that Christ considered Himself the Messiah. And now He was claiming that God the Father was preparing to make Christ's enemies His footstool. And who were His enemies?

These lawyers and Pharisees were. He made no secret of that.

Perhaps the Pharisees understood exactly what Christ was talking about. It's no coincidence that, following this incident, they intensified their conspiracy to have Him betrayed and killed.

The dispute has come full circle. It started in that small house in Capernaum when Jesus had the audacity to pronounce the forgiveness of the paralytic's sins. *Blasphemy!* the Pharisees thought. Christ addressed it head-on. He demonstrated divine power. "But so you may know that the Son of Man has authority on earth to forgive sins...get up, pick up your stretcher, and go home'" (Matthew 9:6).

And now, three years later, Jesus was reminding them that the Messiah sits at the right hand of God the Father, above all of creation, including the great King David. A mere man? Or a divine being on equal footing with God?

Blasphemy! they must have thought again.

They had always been willing to tolerate Jesus as a prophet. But this claim of deity, made not just at this time but on prior occasions as well, was way over the top. He would have to pay. Before Roman occupation, the penalty would have been fast and certain. But now things were considerably more complicated. Nonetheless, these claims of supremacy could not be tolerated.

Two Thousand Years Later...

"The more things change," said Yogi Berra, "the more things remain the same." Today the claims of Christ that rile people the most are still His claims of supremacy. "I am *the* way," He said. "My enemies will become My footstool."

Lee Strobel, a former atheist turned apologist for the Christian faith, describes the mind-set of our culture toward these claims:

> Many people consider it arrogant, narrow-minded, and bigoted for Christians to contend that the only path to God must go through Jesus of Nazareth. In a day of religious pluralism and tolerance, this exclusivity claim is politically incorrect, a verbal slap in the face of other belief systems. Pluralist Rosemary Radford Ruether labeled it "absurd religious chauvinism."[6]

Lee understands this thinking entirely, because he felt the same way prior to his conversion. "When I was an atheist, I bristled at assertions by Christians that they held a monopoly on the only correct approach to religion. 'Who do they think they are?' I'd grouse. 'Who are they to judge everyone else?'"[7]

Nor is this a recent phenomena. For hundreds of years, men and women have been trying to water down Jesus and sand off His rough edges, especially the rough edges of exclusivity and superiority. His teachings go down much better to some if we redact the miraculous and turn Him into just another wise teacher. As good as other prophets, yes. But no better.

Our country was founded during the so-called Enlightenment, or Age of Reason. The design of this movement was to "declare the autonomy of the human mind and so to replace revelation with reason, dogma with science, the supernatural with the natural, and a pessimistic view of the human condition with confidence in the fundamental goodness of human nature."[8]

Thomas Jefferson, one of its adherents, quite literally applied this philosophy with scissors and paste to the New Testament. He cut out all the miracles of Christ, creating a work he entitled *The Life and Morals of Jesus of Nazareth.* He was left with only Jesus's teachings, grouped by topic.[9] For Jefferson, it was a logical thing to take out the miraculous, leaving the reader with only the pure teachings of Jesus, separating "what is really His from the rubbish in which it is buried... the diamond from the dunghill."[10]

Jefferson's makeshift Bible, of course, ends with Christ's death. Is this the real Jesus? How do you separate His teachings from His miracles—something that Jesus Himself was unwilling to do? To prove He could forgive sins, Christ healed the paralytic. When the Pharisees wanted a sign, Christ pointed to the Resurrection. To strip the miracles from Christ's teachings is to perform *Hamlet* without the prince. I'm not sure what's left in Jefferson's Bible, but it's not the Jesus of recorded history. A tame Jesus—maybe. A less offensive Christ—for sure. But also one who has no power to forgive our sins or rescue us from death.

Even the more "enlightened" thinkers of the Enlightenment,

those with a higher view of Christ, still didn't get it quite right. Consider, for example, the lofty-sounding rhetoric of French philosopher Joseph-Ernest Renan: " 'Let us place, then, the person of Jesus at the highest summit of human greatness.' For among the 'uniform mediocrity' of humankind 'there are pillars that rise towards the sky.... Jesus is the highest of these pillars.' "[11]

High praise, but not high enough. Jesus didn't speak of Himself as another pillar rising head and shoulders above the pillars of other men. He talked about being on a whole different plane. "The Father and I are one," He said (John 10:30). On another occasion, "Before Abraham was, I am" (John 8:58). And here, at the end of His ministry, Jesus was claiming His divine prerogative—equality with God, preeminence over all humanity. "I am the Christ, high and lifted up, sitting at the right hand of the Father since the beginning of time."

Loving the Lord God with all your heart, soul, mind, and strength is a good start. But, as Jesus reminded the lawyer, this can't quite get you to the kingdom of God. "You're not far off," Jesus said. But there was one more thing. It had to do with the role of the Messiah, the One whom even David called "Lord."

Take Him or leave Him as He is, but don't water Him down. Study the life of Christ and the lives of other religious leaders. Look at His impact. Think about His teachings. Put Him to the test. You've seen throughout this book how He bucked the religious establishment of His day. How He cared about people more than rules. How He hung out with society's rejects. How He confounded society's wise men. How He surprised the skeptics and silenced the critics. How He kept His promises, including that little matter about rising from the dead after three days and three nights.

Does this sound like just another prophet or like the kind of Savior you can trust? Noted apologist Ravi Zacharias puts it this way:

No man spoke like Jesus. No one ever answered the questions the way he answered them, not only propositionally, but also in his person. Existentially, we can test it out. Empirically, we can test it out. The Bible is not just a book of mysticism or spirituality; it is a book that also gives geographical truths and historical truths. If you're an honest skeptic, it's not just calling you to a feeling; it's calling you to a real Person. That's why the apostle Peter said, "We did not follow cleverly invented stories when we told you about the power and coming of our Lord Jesus Christ, but we were eyewitnesses of his majesty."

He is saying, "This is true. This is reality. This can be trusted."[12]

The Pharisees didn't think so. They didn't dare ask Jesus any more questions, but they weren't finished yet, either. In their minds, Jesus had pushed too far, claiming equality with God and predicting complete victory over His enemies.

In the next chapter, we'll see where that ultimately took Him. Returning to the scene we left in chapter 1, we'll follow Jesus to His final cross-examination.

10

ROME V. JESUS OF NAZARETH
(THE VERDICT)

On the way back to the praetorium, your stomach still sickened from watching the brutal flogging of Christ, you bump into Joseph of Arimathea. He is the last person you want to see. He falls in beside you, struggling to keep up with your swift pace.

"I know you're doing what you can," he says, huffing.

"I tried," you say. "But it was not enough."

"I hate to even ask—but could you do one more thing for me, Octavian?"

You can't believe that this man, friend though he is, has the audacity to ask another favor. You've already stuck your neck out way too far. You decide to let silence be your answer.

"Could you ask Pilate if I could give the body a decent burial?" Joseph says.

The request takes you off-guard. "He's not dead yet, Joseph." You look at your friend and see the pain etched on his face. "And besides, right now, I'm not the man you want asking Pilate for a favor."

You arrive at the gate to the praetorium. Joseph faces you and gives you the embrace of a friend. "You've been a good friend, Octavian."

"I'm sorry," you say as you turn and head inside.

Pilate has been waiting for you. You find him pacing in his study, his face flushed with the pressures of the moment. "Where have you been?" he barks.

You look him dead in the eye. "Watching the chastisement of an innocent man."

He turns on you, moving a step closer. "Are you lecturing me? Do you think I enjoy this?"

"No, Your Excellency."

Pilate is now in your face, so close you can smell the wine on his breath—was that just a few short hours ago?—and almost taste his fear. You've seen him like this before, breathing in staccato, his eyes narrowing into paranoid slits.

Pilate is a big man, every bit as tall as you but much heavier. He is in his intimidation mode, posturing here in front of you. You do not meet his eyes, choosing instead to gaze slightly downward.

"Have you ever commanded on a field of battle, Octavian Faustus?"

"No, Your Excellency. I have dedicated my life to the law."

"If you had, you would know that you must sometimes sacrifice the life of one man for the good of the army. You sometimes sacrifice an entire battalion. These are hard decisions, but they are decisions commanders must make."

"On the battlefield that may be true, but in a court of law, we seek justice."

"Don't speak to me about justice!" Pilate hisses, showering your face with his spit. "Your brand of justice has already released Barabbas, a man who murdered a Roman soldier. Do you think Rome will be impressed by the clever gamesmanship of Octavian Faustus?"

You stand silently, but you do not cower. You have learned today from the courage of the Galilean.

"Do you?" Pilate demands.

"No, Your Excellency."

"And neither do I." Pilate starts pacing again, lowering the tension in the room by a notch.

"How bad is he?" Pilate asks, his tone less hostile.

"Unrecognizable. Inhuman."

"Good." Pilate stops pacing and glances out the window at the restless crowd. "We'll parade Him in front of His people one more time and see if this satisfies their blood lust." Pilate shakes his head ruefully, as if he cannot understand the hatred that has consumed this crowd. "If it doesn't, we have no choice but to sanction His death. Do you agree?"

You stand there frozen as Pilate's desperate eyes turn to you. This situation has spun so wildly out of control. You want to plead for this man's life—tell Pilate to act like a Roman and resist the mob—but you know your plea would fall on deaf ears. Worse, hostile ears. Jesus is a dead man; that much is plain. The only issue now is whether you're willing to go down with Him.

And for what? you wonder. *To honor a justice system that has already released a murderer and flogged an innocent man? To defend a madman who claims He is the Son of God?*

You have fought the good fight. Justice requires no more.

"I agree, Your Excellency."

"BEHOLD, YOUR KING!"

Pilate shouts it to the mob as the soldiers drag Jesus to the Stone Pavement and parade Him in front of the crowd. His form is hideous—face scarred and swollen, the crown of thorns digging deep into His scalp, the robe of Herod draped around His shoulders. You realize that even now the rich fabric will be adhering to the open sores and gaping wounds, thereby creating more pain when it is ripped off. You cannot bear to look at Him for long.

The chief priests and temple police are yelling for His crucifixion, but you hardly hear them. It feels like you are no longer part of the events unfolding before you, like you are powerless to stop this relentless march of history.

"We have a law," someone yells, "and according to that law He must die, because He made Himself the Son of God."

This comment, more than any of the others, seems to startle Pilate. The next thing you know, he has recessed the proceedings and taken the prisoner back into his headquarters. As before, you have joined them, just a few feet away from this suffering man. Amazingly, Jesus's composure has not changed, though the pain must be excruciating.

Pilate doesn't waste time. "Where are You from?"

A strange question, you think. Does Pilate have more jurisdictional maneuverings in mind, or is he really starting to buy this "Son of God" talk? The note from Claudia lies ominously on Pilate's desk.

But Jesus doesn't answer. It's maddening, His refusal to plead for His own life. How can you help someone who seems so intent on dying?

Pilate must be thinking the same thing. "You're not talking to me?" Pilate rants. "Don't You know that I have the authority to release You and the authority to crucify You?"

You will never forget the calmness of Jesus's response. "You would have no authority over Me at all if it hadn't been given you from above," He says, nearly whispering through swollen lips. "This is why the one who handed Me over to you has the greater sin."

The prisoner then turns to you. One eye is nearly swollen shut, a grotesque purple bulge pressuring the eyelid. But there is no hatred in His eyes, no condemnation. Fear is totally lacking. If anything, His eyes register concern.

For you? How can He be concerned for you? He's the one facing the Cross.

Pilate seems resigned to giving this man over. And you can think of no way out for Him this time. You follow Pilate and Jesus back to the Stone Pavement, where the crowd is more intense than ever. "Anyone who makes himself a king opposes Caesar!" they shout, understanding Pilate's weakness. "We have no king but Caesar!"

Pilate finally grants the crowd their wish. Jesus is hauled away by Roman guards, surrounded by the mob, as Pilate turns his back on the proceeding. You watch in disbelief as the soldiers lead Jesus from the courtyard, heading for Calvary, the place the Jews call Golgotha. You stare straight ahead in stunned disbelief as the crowd disperses, following the prisoner. Some time later, maybe minutes later, maybe an hour or so, you realize that you're the only one left.

You have dedicated your life to the study of law, but you sense that from this day forward things will never be the same. The law was powerless to protect this man from mob rule. Is this Roman justice?

Images from the morning flash through your thoughts. The angry crowd. A silent prisoner. A brutal flogging. A gutless procurator. These images stalk you—one after the other, a ceaseless cycle of shame.

There are two in particular that have seared themselves into your memory. The first is the image of your own acquiescence to this miscarriage of justice—"I agree, Your Excellency." How can you live with yourself now? The second is more haunting still—the eyes of the prisoner when He looked at you in Pilate's headquarters. Eyes of compassion, if that's even possible.

Somehow you feel like you knew this man. And you can't shake the feeling that, in reality, you're the one who condemned Him to die.

You journey back to your own residence and try to busy yourself with routine legal matters. It is useless. You are a man consumed by the day's drama. You find yourself pacing your study, staring out toward the north—the rugged hills overlooking Jerusalem. It is there, at the Place of the Skull, where the prisoner will be drawing His last breaths.

You find yourself wondering what is happening even now. Did Joseph get permission to bury the man? Did Jesus even make it to the cross, or did He die en route?

You have watched one crucifixion from beginning to end. Studied it, really. It was a required part of your legal training—an appreciation of the cruel consequences of your decisions.

You have passed by dozens of others. A year ago you watched as the soldiers crucified a woman—one who had allegedly plotted against Pilate. She hung naked for three days before she died. They let her body rot for another day before they took her down from the cross and threw her into the mass grave at Hinnom Valley. Disgusted, you vowed never to witness another crucifixion. But today, notwithstanding that vow, you find yourself inexorably drawn to the Place of the Skull.

You've Got to See Him Again

You arrive fifteen minutes before noon, nearly three hours since you last saw Jesus. Golgotha is on a craggy hillside next to a major thoroughfare on the northern side of Jerusalem. The Hebrew name refers to the rocky hill shaped like a skull where crucifixions traditionally take place, close enough to the road so those walking by can mock the criminals. Today there are three crosses on the hill, with Jesus hanging in the middle. On each side of Him are common thieves—men who just last week received fair Roman trials. Those proceedings seem like an eternity ago.

The crowd has thinned some, though the chief priests and elders are still there, mocking the Galilean. The others seem to have lost some of their vehemence. Roman soldiers form a semicircle around the foot of the cross, keeping the onlookers at bay. You see Joseph with another Jewish leader, a man you know as Nicodemus, off to one side, talking quietly.

You take a spot at the back of the crowd and gaze up at Jesus. Blood drips from the spikes in each wrist and the ones driven through

His feet. You can tell by His color that His time is short—grayish skin and the blue lips of a shock victim. Jesus can breathe only with great difficulty, pushing Himself up by pressing against the nails in His feet, scraping His bloodied back against the coarse wood of the cross. He will spasmodically rise, contort His face in anguish, suck in an uncertain breath, and let His body drop again. He moans in pain with each labored breath.

His nakedness and the crown of thorns complete His humiliation. Above His head is an inscription Pilate authorized:

THIS IS JESUS
THE KING OF THE JEWS

"He saved others, but He cannot save Himself!" someone shouts.

"Let Him come down now from the cross, and we will believe in Him!"

Others murmur their agreement.

"Has it been going on like this the whole time?" you ask the woman next to you. Your eyes, however, remain fixed on Jesus.

"It was worse at the beginning," she replies. "Even the thieves on both sides threw insults at Him. But then…" Her voice trails off. She places her head in her hands as you turn, resisting the urge to embrace and comfort her.

"He prayed for the forgiveness of everyone mocking Him," says her companion, completing the thought. "Things settled down some after that."

You have no response. What can be said about such a man? In

awe, you listen to the scornful voices in front of you and watch this remarkable Galilean who returns forgiveness for hate.

Before long, the crowd appears to grow restless with the death-watch and the mocking intensifies. The soldiers join in this time, offering Jesus sour wine on a sponge hoisted to His mouth by a spear. "If You are the King of the Jews, save Yourself!"

Still, Jesus remains silent in the face of such hatred.

One of the thieves, gasping for breath, joins the refrain again, hurling vile insults at Jesus. *What right do you have to insult the innocent?* you wonder. But you withhold your rebuke. What good would it do?

The thief on the other side of Jesus does not withhold his. "Don't you even fear God?" he asks the first thief. "We are punished justly, because we're getting back what we deserve for the things we did, but this man has done nothing wrong."

The thief pushes himself up for a breath, his face twisted in pain. He pauses, then turns to Jesus. You can hardly hear his words: "Jesus, remember me when You come into Your kingdom."

You watch, leaning forward and straining to hear, as Jesus turns to face the man. You could swear that the swollen and cracked lips try to register a smile. "I assure you," Jesus gasps. "Today you will be with Me in paradise."

You are mesmerized, waiting for more. But there is no more. Jesus returns to the task of drawing excruciating breaths. The thief appears satisfied.

A few minutes later, you see Jesus speak a few words to a man and several women who have been allowed to approach the foot of the cross. The women are crying, and you find yourself on the verge of tears as well. *I don't even know this man!* you remind yourself.

At noon the clouds roll in. The intense brightness of the Judean sun gives way to a storm gathering to the west. The sky darkens as the barren landscape whips into a gray frenzy, peppering the remaining crowd with grains of sand. The soldiers use their shields to cover their faces from the *khamsin,* the black, swirling wind that blows in buckets of sand from the nearby wilderness. It carries with it the stench of the temple sacrifices, the burning skin of bleating animals that nearly gags you. Instinctively, you turn your back on the windstorm, covering your head with the sleeve of your toga. You think about the body of Jesus, exposed on the cross.

Within minutes the wind has stopped, leaving an eerie stillness. Remarkably, the darkness does not lift. This is more than the gray skies of a midafternoon storm. The crosses have become mere silhouettes, the shame of nakedness hidden by a midnight shroud.

Nobody speaks for several long minutes. The signs are unmistakable, even to a Roman. The gods are not pleased. You stand there astonished, unsure whether you can even trust your senses. A few of the remaining religious leaders try to resume a conversation, as if nothing unusual has happened. But an awkward silence soon engulfs the crowd. Voices are lowered, as if the darkness carries with it a mandate to stop the mocking. You can almost reach out and touch the fear that settles on those around you. Many quietly walk away, picking their path through the darkness, as if by leaving now they will avoid the full fury of God.

You stay, bewildered at the sight before you. Minutes race by as you acclimate your eyes to the midday darkness. You half expect Jesus to climb down from the cross. The miracles spoken of by Joseph earlier in the day no longer seem so unlikely.

But it does not happen. One hour bleeds into two and then into three. Jesus's movements are more spasmodic and labored. A soldier lights a torch to check on Him. The blood continues to drip from the Galilean, some spattering on the arm of the centurion. Strangely, he doesn't bother to wipe it off. Jesus's breathing is short and shallow; tiny gasps of breath are interrupted by excruciating pain. Between breaths, His body hangs at a tortured angle—His arms nearly ripped from their sockets, the nails tearing at the tendons in His wrists.

For some reason you cannot leave. You will never forget the surreal feeling of standing there in the dark, your eyes riveted to the struggling silhouette of Jesus, listening to the subdued taunts of gloating enemies and the quiet sobbing of family and friends.

After three hours, Jesus cries out to His heavenly Father, shocking you with the intensity of His cry. A few minutes later, in a hoarse, dry voice, He complains of thirst. A soldier lifts a sponge soaked in vinegar to Jesus's lips. But Jesus lets out another loud cry—"It is finished!"—and raises Himself up for one last, fitful breath.

The next moment, fading fast, He gasps His final words: "Father, into Your hands I entrust My spirit!"

A lump rises in your throat as you watch Jesus quietly bow His head. He ceases His struggle. His chest stops moving in and out. His body hangs like a rag.

And you are not prepared for what follows…

The Moment of Truth

The earth rumbles, then shakes, rocks splitting in two. You crouch on the ground, trying to get your bearings in the darkness. The centurion at the foot of the cross, unable to contain himself, blurts out his own confession: "This man really was God's Son!"

The darkness begins to lift and you look around, realizing that this rocky hillside has been transformed into a chamber of justice. You rise to your feet as all around you men and women are rendering their verdicts. A centurion worships. A priest scowls and shakes his head as he leaves. Joseph and Nicodemus are on their faces, repenting.

Even the other criminals were not immune. They are both dead now. But one made his peace with Jesus before he died; the other did not.

You realize with awful certainty that you're the one who sealed this innocent man's fate. Sure, the Jewish leaders brought the charges. But the Roman system failed to deliver justice. You acquiesced, putting your own well-being above the life of a godly man.

Suddenly, it occurs to you that you, too, must choose sides. To walk away now is to reject Him again. Kneeling before Him may cost you everything. Surely word would get back to Pilate. But somehow you sense that walking away might cost you more.

Pilate's question rings in your mind: "What is truth?" The soldier cries out in worship, calling Jesus the "Son of God" over and over. The high priest raises his voice in response, quoting the Hebrew Scriptures: "Anyone who is hung on a tree is under God's curse."

Accursed by God or God's own Son?

Your legal training cautions against precipitous action. A centurion can yield to the emotions of the moment—but a lawyer? The mockers have a point: if this is God's Son, why didn't He defend Himself? Why did He insist on such fatalistic silence?

Your heart suggests an answer, but it doesn't make sense. *For some inexplicable reason, He did this for you!*

"What is truth?" Pilate asked.

You swallow hard, consider the consequences, and render your verdict.

NOTES

INTRODUCTION

1. John Henry Wigmore, *Evidence in Trials at Common Law,* 3rd ed. (Boston: Little, Brown, 1940), sec. 1367, 29.

CHAPTER ONE

1. There is some uncertainty about trial rules for the Sanhedrin in first-century Jerusalem. Later records describe these Jewish trial procedures, and it is probable that substantially the same rules were in place when Christ was tried. The Talmud (oral tradition tacked onto the Mosaic Law) is chock-full of procedural safeguards for capital offenses, most of which were violated in the trial of Jesus. They include: (1) The accused had the right against self-incrimination—he could not be asked questions at his trial. (2) Two witnesses were required in capital cases, and their testimonies had to agree on every detail. (3) If witnesses perjured themselves, they were given the same punishment as the original defendant. (4) Capital trials were required to be conducted between the morning temple sacrifice and the evening temple sacrifice. (5) Judges were to be defenders of the accused or else a court-appointed advocate—a balil rib—was appointed. In either event, judges could not serve as prosecutors. (6) Guilty verdicts had to be by a two-vote margin, and no unanimous verdicts were allowed, as this would be a sign of a

mob-rule mentality. (7) Trials were to be held continuously (no recesses so advocates could "fix" testimony), but a guilty verdict and ultimate sentence could not be handed down on the same day. This would give judges a chance to "sleep on it"—pray and seek the Lord's guidance without being pressured by the heat of the trial (Leith Anderson, *Jesus* [Minneapolis: Bethany, 2005], 318–19).

2. Gordon Thomas, *The Jesus Conspiracy: An Investigative Reporter's Look at an Extraordinary Life and Death* (Grand Rapids, MI: Baker, 1997), 224.

CHAPTER TWO

1. The Greek word for "scribes" is *grammateus.* In New Testament times, a *grammateus* examined the more difficult and subtle questions of the Mosaic Law, adding his own interpretations to clarify the meaning. In this sense, the scribes were experts and teachers in the Law and the functional equivalent of religious lawyers.

2. C. S. Lewis, *Mere Christianity* (San Francisco: HarperSan Francisco, 2001), 52.

3. "Jack London," *The Literature Network,* www.online-literature .com/london.

CHAPTER THREE

1. Gene A. Veal, "The Mind of Christ: His View of Pharisees," www.seegod.org/his_view_of_pharisees.htm.

2. Richard J. Foster, *Celebration of Discipline,* rev. ed. (San Francisco: Harper and Row, 1988), 48.

3. Foster, *Celebration,* 48.

4. Donald S. Whitney, *Spiritual Disciplines for the Christian Life* (Colorado Springs CO: NavPress, 1992), 157–8.

5. The same principles, of course, apply to abstaining from any desire of the flesh or luxuries for the purpose of drawing closer to God. Thus, some Christians "fast" from television or from some other form of entertainment or a favorite hobby for a length of time.

6. Foster, *Celebration,* 59.

7. Matthew 12:8–14; Mark 3:1–6; Luke 13:10–17; 14:1–6; John 5:1–9; 9:1–16.

8. Exodus 16:23.

9. Isaiah 66:23.

10. There is, of course, doctrinal debate on what day constitutes the Sabbath in modern society. Though that issue is beyond the scope of this brief discussion, Christ's admonition to stay focused on the spirit of the Law would seem to apply here as well.

CHAPTER FOUR

1. Quoted in Michael Green, *Men Alive* (Downers Grove, IL: InterVarsity, 1968), 54.

2. Frank Harber, *Reasons for Believing* (Green Forest, AR: New Leaf, 1998), 67.

3. Ralph O. Muncaster, *The Bible: General Analysis* (Mission Viejo, CA: Strong Basis to Believe, 1996), 13.

4. Ralph O. Muncaster, *The Bible: Manuscript Reliability* (Mission Viejo, CA: Strong Basis to Believe, 1997), 23.

5. Ralph O. Muncaster, *Evidence for Jesus* (Eugene, OR: Harvest House: 2004), 101.

6. Muncaster, *Evidence for Jesus,* 101.

7. Ben Witherington III, *The Gospel Code: Novel Claims About Jesus, Mary Magdalene, and Da Vinci* (Downers Grove, IL: InterVarsity, 2004), 50.

8. Witherington, *Gospel Code,* 52.

9. Witherington, *Gospel Code,* 35.

10. Muncaster, *Evidence for Jesus,* 111–13.

11. "Is the Bible True?" *U.S. News and World Report,* 25 October 1999, www.uhcg.org/news/is=bible=true.html.

12. William Ramsey, *St. Paul: The Travels of a Roman Citizen* (Grand Rapids, MI: Baker, 1962), 36.

13. William Ramsey, *The Bearing of Recent Discoveries on the Trustworthiness of the New Testament* (Grand Rapids, MI: Baker, 1953), 222.

14. Muncaster (quoting Eusebius, *Church History*), *Evidence for Jesus,* 34.

15. Alexander Metherell, quoted in Lee Strobel, *The Case for Christ: A Journalist's Personal Investigation of the Evidence for Jesus* (Grand Rapids, MI: Zondervan, 1998), 195–96.

16. Strobel, *Case for Christ,* 198–99.

17. "The Search for Jesus," *ABC Special Report,* 26 June 2000.

18. See also Luke 9:22: "The Son of Man...[will] be raised on the third day."

CHAPTER SIX

1. Bonnie C. Harvey, *Charles Finney: The Great Revivalist* (Uhrichsville, OH: Barbour, 1999), 23.

2. When some members of Finney's church wanted to make him a special object of prayer, the pastor advised against it. "I do not believe Finney will ever be converted," he said (Charles G. Finney, *Revival Lectures* [Grand Rapids, MI: Revell, n.d.], 24).

3. Harvey, *Charles Finney,* 35–36.

4. V. Raymond Edman, *Finney on Revival* (Minneapolis: Bethany, 2000), 43.

5. After Christ told the parable of the good Samaritan, Christ asked the lawyer which of the three who passed by the wounded man was his neighbor. In Luke 10:37, the lawyer's answer ("The one who showed mercy") and Christ's response ("Go and do the same") could support a hypothesis that the lawyer was a well-known prosecutor long on judgment and short on mercy.

CHAPTER SEVEN

1. Leonard W. Levy, *The Origins of the Fifth Amendment: The Right Against Self-Incrimination* (New York: Oxford University Press, 1968), 272.

2. Levy, *Origins of the Fifth Amendment,* 272.

3. It's not just Job. For example, Gideon and Jeremiah had a few *why* questions for God as well (see Judges 6:13–14; Jeremiah 12:1, 5).

4. John Horgan, "Quantum Philosophy," *Scientific American,* July 1992, reprinted at www.fortunecity.com/emachines/e11/86/qphil.html.

5. Simon Singh, *The Code Book: The Evolution of Secrecy from Mary, Queen of Scots, to Quantum Cryptography* (New York: Random House, 1999), 324. This book, though dedicated for the most part to an entirely different subject matter, contains the most straightforward explanation of quantum physics I've found.

6. Singh, *Code Book,* 325.

Chapter Eight

1. Later, at Christ's trial in front of Pilate, the Pharisees would raise this same issue, falsely accusing Christ of opposing the payment of taxes to Caesar (see Luke 23:2).

2. Stephen L. Carter, *The Culture of Disbelief: How American Law and Politics Trivialize Religious Devotion* (New York: Bantam Doubleday Dell, 1993), 23–24.

3. Charles Krauthammer, "In Defense of Certainty," *Time,* 6 June 2005, 96.

Chapter Nine

1. Jeffery L. Sheler and others, "Faith in America," *U.S. News and World Report,* 6 May 2002.

2. Many translations refer to the questioner as a "scribe," as opposed to a "lawyer"; for example, ASV, ISV, NKJV, and HCSB. There is, however, no conflict here. Scribes were, by function,

experts in the Law of Moses. They examined the more difficult and subtle questions of the Law and added their own decisions in order to elucidate the Law as they saw it. The Greek word in question, *grammateus,* referred to "a man learned in the Mosaic law and in the sacred writings, an interpreter, teacher" (James Strong, *Strong's Exhaustive Concordance of the Bible* [Nashville: Thomas Nelson, 1990], s.v. "Greek Dictionary," 20).

3. See Psalm 89:35–36; Isaiah 9:6–7.

4. Quotes taken from a speech given by Marvin Olasky to the Council for National Policy on 25 April 2003, as originally documented at www.olasky.com. For more information, see Bob Reccord and Randy Singer, *Made to Count: Discovering What to Do with Your Life* (Nashville: W Publishing, 2004), 62–65.

5. See Matthew 4:4–10; Luke 4:18–19; Matthew 22:44; 26:64; 27:46 (compare Psalm 22:1).

6. Lee Strobel, *The Case for Faith: A Journalist Investigates the Toughest Objections to Christianity* (Grand Rapids, MI: Zondervan, 2000), 146.

7. Strobel, *Case for Faith,* 146.

8. John Stott, *The Incomparable Christ* (Downers Grove, IL: InterVarsity, 2001), 107.

9. Stott, *Incomparable Christ,* 110.

10. Dickenson Adams, *The Papers of Thomas Jefferson,* 2nd series, *Jefferson's Extracts from the Gospels* (Princeton, NJ: Princeton University Press, 1983), 388.

11. Quoted in Stott, *Incomparable Christ,* 109.

12. Quoted in Strobel, *Case for Faith,* 153.

THE
CROSS
EXAMINATION
of OLIVER FINNEY

RANDY SINGER

WATERBROOK
PRESS

THE CROSS EXAMINATION OF OLIVER FINNEY
PUBLISHED BY WATERBROOK PRESS
12265 Oracle Boulevard, Suite 200
Colorado Springs, Colorado 80921
A division of Random House Inc.

Scripture quotations or paraphrases are taken from the following versions: The Amplified® Bible. Copyright © 1954, 1958, 1962, 1964, 1965, 1987 by The Lockman Foundation. Used by permission. (www.Lockman.org). The Holy Bible, English Standard Version, copyright © 2001 by Crossway Bibles, a division of Good News Publishers. Used by permission. All rights reserved. Holman Christian Standard Bible®, © copyright 1999, 2000, 2002, 2003 by Holman Bible Publishers. Used by permission. Holy Bible, New International Version®. NIV®. Copyright © 1973, 1978, 1984 by International Bible Society. Used by permission of Zondervan Publishing House. All rights reserved. New King James Version®. Copyright © 1982 by Thomas Nelson Inc. Used by permission. All rights reserved.

Suras from the Koran are taken from www.hti.umich.edu/k/koran, an electronic version of The Holy Qur'an, translated by M.H. Shakir and published by Tahrike Tarsile Qur'an Inc., in 1983.

The characters and events in this book are fictional, and any resemblance to actual persons or events is coincidental.

ISBN: 0-7394-6750-6
ISBN 13: 978-0-7394-6750-3

Printed in the United States of America

Praise for
The Cross Examination of Oliver Finney

"Randy Singer's *The Cross Examination of Oliver Finney* is that rarest of novels—a thrilling story that makes the reader think as well as feel. A cigar-smoking, plain-talking Christian judge goes on a reality TV show to defend his faith and finds his life threatened in the process—it's a great concept, and Singer has pulled it off with entertaining aplomb. I couldn't put this one down, and you won't be able to either!"

—ANGELA HUNT, author of *Magdalene* and *The Novelist*

"Randy Singer has done it again! He has produced a first-rate legal thriller written from the perspective of a Christian worldview. Intrigue, suspense, and mystery capture the reader's attention. But in the context of unraveling a thoughtful whodunit, a dynamite case for Christianity is articulated. Saint and skeptic alike will find *The Cross Examination of Oliver Finney* to be an informative, intriguing, and challenging must-read. Singer's fictional work is sanctified imagination and informed apologetics at their best."

—DR. PHIL ROBERTS, president of Midwestern Baptist Theological Seminary

"Randy Singer is a talented writer with an incredible ability to bring relevant topics into page-turning fiction. *The Cross Examination of Oliver Finney* is a must-read for all Singer fans and will bring him new fans, too. I thoroughly enjoyed it."

—RENE GUTTERIDGE, author of *Boo, Boo Who,* and *Boo Hiss*

THE
CROSS
EXAMINATION
of OLIVER FINNEY

OTHER BOOKS
BY RANDY SINGER

NOVELS

Directed Verdict
Irreparable Harm
Dying Declaration
Self Incrimination
The Judge Who Stole Christmas

NONFICTION

Made to Count
Live Your Passion, Tell Your Story, Change Your World
The Cross Examination of Jesus Christ

To Jeanine Allen and David O'Malley,
two extraordinary friends who each heard
these coveted words in 2005:

"Well done, good and faithful servant!"
Matthew 25:23, NIV

PART 1

AGENDAS

I'm not afraid of dying. I just don't
want to be there when it happens.
—WOODY ALLEN

They could have done better with an axe.
—GEORGE WESTINGHOUSE, after witnessing
the first use of the electric chair

CHAPTER 1

There must be some mistake.

The room started spinning as soon as the Patient heard the words. *Inoperable brain cancer. Frontal lobe.*

He gripped the arms of the chair and began the denial process immediately. He never trusted this doctor in the first place and now...he could swear the doctor smirked when he told him. All doctors, even highly paid oncologists, envied the Patient. Hated the Patient. The doctor was wrong, his judgment blurred by a subconscious bias. Men the Patient's age do not get brain cancer. Especially men who run three times a week and drink one glass of red wine every evening.

Do not. Cannot.

In the ensuing days, the Patient would get a second and third opinion. The top oncologists at the best hospitals in the country, all singing from the same song sheet. "We're sorry, there's nothing we can do. Chemo might slow the spread of the disease, but you probably have less than a year." They ticked off symptoms like a parade of horrors: behavioral changes, impaired judgment, memory loss, reduced cognitive function, vision loss, partial paralysis.

The Patient worked quickly through the stages of acceptance. Denial turned to anger. Tragedy seemed to stalk the Patient's family. His mother died from a stroke when the Patient was in college. His sister lost a teenage son in a freak motorboat accident. A first cousin died before her thirty-fifth birthday. And now this. But anger eventually gave way to grief and then ultimately resignation—all within a span of four weeks. Yet he wasn't prepared for the last stage, and he couldn't shake the irony of it.

Remorse. Nearly a billion dollars in net assets that he couldn't take with him. Today he would trade all of his wealth for one additional year. All the eighty-hour weeks, jetting around the country, the dog-eat-dog world he faced every day, the enemies he had made—everything he did to build the net wealth so he could one day retire early and enjoy life. And now he had twelve months.

He started getting his affairs in order. He signed a living will and durable power of attorney, spurred by the knowledge that he might lose his sanity before he drew his last breath. He changed his last will and testament a dozen times but eventually lost his enthusiasm for disinheriting the estranged children of his first and second wives. For the most part, they were young and firmly in the clutches of their overbearing and greedy mothers. No sense punishing the children. He changed it one final time and made each child a millionaire, even his rebellious fourteen-year-old daughter who reminded him way too much of her mother.

The one thing he couldn't prepare for preoccupied his thoughts day and night, night and day. He wasn't ready to face whatever lurked on the other side of death. He tried praying to some vague notion of God but just felt silly. What kind of God would listen to a man who had spent his whole life denying that God existed? Yet the thought of stepping into the darkness of death without solving life's greatest mystery scared the Patient most of all. If he were God, he would judge his own life harshly. Sure, he had accumulated vast amounts of wealth, but what *good* had he done? Who would say that life on earth was better because they had known him?

The sad and honest truth kept him awake at night and haunted his daytime thoughts. Maybe there was still time. A lot could be done in twelve months. But even if he wanted to curry favor with God, how could he do that? He still didn't really believe that God existed. And if God did exist, which of the gods worshiped on planet Earth was the true God?

It hit him while watching *Survivor,* nearly four weeks after the initial diagnosis. Life's greatest reality show! It seemed like such a deliciously good idea that it was either a stroke of genius or the brain cancer deluding him ahead of schedule. Powerful advocates for each of the world's major religions would be chosen as contestants. Their faith would be put to the ultimate test on a remote island. They would be forced into the trial of their lives: defending their faith against all challenges. The winner's god would gain a whole raft of new adherents, including the Patient. He would donate millions to the right causes. The ratings for the show would be spectacular.

The losers' gods would be exposed as impotent—powerless frauds in the face of death.

CHAPTER 2

Nikki Moreno leaned around the folks in the back of the long line at the Norfolk Courthouse metal detector, propped her sunglasses on top of her head, and caught the attention of one of the sheriff's deputies. She flashed her famous Moreno smile, and he waved her to the front. D. J. Landers, a sleazy defense attorney who had caught up with Nikki in the parking lot, followed hot on her heels. Too hot, in Nikki's opinion. He had already hit on her twice, and now he chattered in her ear as if they were best friends, undoubtedly realizing that Nikki was his ticket to the front of the line.

"I'm five minutes late already," Landers said. "But as fate would have it, my hearing's in front of Judge Finney, and I just happen to bump into his beautiful and talented law clerk this morning in the parking lot." Landers made a little "tsk-tsk" noise to emphasize what an incredible stroke of luck this was. "Hey, maybe she'll cover for me. Tell the judge she insisted I fix her breakfast after last night."

Nikki snorted without turning around. "We've got to get you off those mind-altering drugs," she said, placing her briefcase on the belt. She sashayed through the detector, content to let the deputies ogle every inch of her long legs and masterfully designed body. Landers, on the other hand, gave her the creeps. She could feel his beady little vulture eyes drilling into her from behind, and she wanted to slap him.

"I've got this one," said one of the beefy deputies. "Total pat down. She looks dangerous."

"You have no idea," Nikki shot back, picking up her briefcase as she graced the deputies with another smile. These guys were her buds, enjoying the friendship that develops between a law student clerking at the courthouse and the deputies who guard it. An *attractive, young* law student, that is. One not afraid to push the upper limits on skirt length or make a fashion statement with ankle and shoulder tattoos.

Before heading away from the guards, Nikki turned to address the annoyance who had slithered through the metal detector behind her. Landers was tall and bony, forty-five or so, with a spray-on tan, a thin black mustache, and jet-black Grecian Formula hair slicked straight back. His face was all angles and bones, and Landers somehow always managed to look like he hadn't shaved in a day and a half—no more, no less.

"Good luck on your prisoner lawsuits," Nikki offered, referring to the well-known practice of prisoners suing the sheriff's department for alleged abuse. Landers looked stunned. He hadn't said a word about any kind of prisoner suit. "A huge verdict might put an end to using Tasers altogether," Nikki continued. "I had no idea how dangerous they were."

"Huh?" Landers said, reaching for his briefcase. But a deputy already had a hand on it.

"Better run this through again," the deputy said. "And sir, I'll need you to step back through there as well."

The other deputy winked at Nikki as she took off down the hallway. She felt safe with these guys around.

"Have a great day," Nikki said over her shoulder, never doubting that the eyes of the deputies would follow her down the hallway as far as humanly possible.

∽

Judge Oliver G. Finney opened the proceedings in Courtroom 3 with a five-minute tongue-lashing of Landers for being late, topped off with a fifteen-hundred-dollar fine—a hundred bucks per minute. "And that's generous," claimed Finney. He motioned to the prosecutor. "Mr. Taylor's time alone is worth twice that much."

Landers gave Nikki a "Say something" look, but Nikki immersed herself in the papers in front of her that suddenly required immediate attention.

Just before court, Finney, who in his spare time wrote test questions for the puzzles and games section of the Law School Admissions Test, had given her some sample questions to try. "You know I stink at these," she protested.

"Precisely why I give them to you," Finney replied. "If you get more than twenty-five percent of the answers correct, I know the questions are too easy."

Landers tendered his check, and Finney got down to the real business at hand. Nikki had glanced at the docket sheet earlier and knew that the defendant, a guy named Terrel Stokes, faced several drug charges that could earn him twenty years minimum. He slouched low in his seat at the counsel table, his movement restricted by handcuffs and leg irons. Despite the restraints and the orange jumpsuit that identified him as just one more accused felon, arrogance leached from the man like body odor.

"We are here today," said Finney, "because the government's key witness in this case was brutally murdered. The prosecution wants to use a prior written statement from the witness at trial, and the defense objects. Does that about sum it up, gentlemen?"

As the lawyers voiced their agreement and discussed procedural issues, Nikki turned her attention to the impossible word puzzle Finney had given her about where certain people sit on a bus given certain parameters. *Arlene never sits next to Bill but will always take a seat beside Carli or Daphne. Daphne always sits in front of either Ella or Carli. If Carli sits next to the window in the second row and Daphne sits across the aisle, then Ella must sit...*

Nikki thought about it for a few seconds, grunted in frustration, and circled choice D. Last time, she had gone with straight Bs, and Finney had accused her of not trying. This time, she would vary her answers.

Finney brought her back to the present with one of his increasingly common coughing fits. He held up his hand to the lawyers, managed a "Hold up a second," then dipped his head and started hacking away. It was a deep and phlegmy cough, and it worried Nikki. A few seconds later, he regained control, though he still wheezed a little as he sucked in air.

Nikki's judge was fifty-nine and starting to show his age, though his lean face still carried vestiges of the sharp and handsome features Nikki had observed on old Bar Association portraits. Finney had lost most of his hair on top, but you hardly noticed the long forehead because the deep-set blue eyes demanded your attention, sparkling with mischief when Finney smiled or slicing you like lasers when he frowned. The eyes were rimmed by thick auburn eyebrows laced, like Finney's hair and long side-burns, with distinguished amounts of gray.

Finney was forever an enigma to Nikki—battle-tested and demand-ing in the courtroom, but an everyday Joe outside. He wore his hair longer than most men his age, so that it curled out a little at the ends, the only part not flattened into place by an old John Deere cap Finney insisted on wearing outside court. If you ran into Finney on the street, you might guess he was a NASCAR fan, but hardly a judge.

"You okay?" asked Mitchell Taylor as the judge regained his compo-sure and took a big gulp of water.

"Fine, fine," said Finney with a flick of the wrist. But Nikki knew that the coughing spells were increasing in both regularity and intensity. She wanted to strangle the judge for refusing to give up cigars. "Continue," he said.

Mitchell Taylor looked down at his notes and picked up at the precise spot where he had left off. Always prepared. Never flustered. A buttoned-down prosecutor who had recently transferred to Norfolk from Virginia Beach. He would have been near the top of Nikki's hottie list but for the fact that he was happily married.

"The facts for this hearing are essentially undisputed," said Mitchell.

He picked up an enlarged photograph mounted on poster board. "This is Antoine Carter," he said, waving the life-size picture of a face caked in blood. "The coroner says he choked to death on his own blood." Mitchell placed the photo facedown on his counsel table while Landers furiously scribbled notes. Stokes sneered at Mitchell, his lips curling slightly upward with a maddening nonchalance, as if he had a Get Out of Jail Free card.

But Mitchell was a pro, too battle hardened to give the defendant even the satisfaction of a glance. "Marks on the victim's wrists and ankles, and around his chest and neck, led the coroner to conclude that he was bound hand and foot and forced to lie on his back, duct-taped to a table, while blood pooled in his throat and ultimately his lungs."

Now Mitchell unveiled another picture, one that made even Nikki divert her eyes, though she had pretty much seen it all. Finney didn't flinch.

"This is a closeup of the victim, Antoine Carter, with his mouth propped open," said Mitchell. "As you can see, his tongue has been cut out."

The deputy sheriff assigned to the courtroom turned her head, and the court reporter went pale. Only Detective Jenkins, a homicide investigator who had accompanied Mitchell to court in case the judge needed testimony, appeared as unaffected as Finney. Nikki forgot all about where her hypothetical passengers might have been sitting on her hypothetical bus. *Who would do such a thing?*

As if reading her mind, Mitchell grabbed a third blow-up from his counsel table. Even as her stomach tightened, morbid curiosity forced Nikki to keep her eyes glued to the young prosecutor and what he might reveal next. "We believe this killing is gang related. This is a picture of Mr. Carter's chest," Mitchell said, his voice tense with anger. "As you can see, the initials BGD are carved into his skin. The blood that coagulated around these cuts indicates Mr. Carter was still alive when they did this.

"BGD stands for the Black Gangster Disciples," said Mitchell, who firmed his jaw and turned to the defendant. "It's one of the strongest gangs operating in Norfolk right now, and we have reason to believe that the defendant, Terrel Stokes, is its leader." At this Stokes grunted his disapproval, then narrowed his eyes and slowly shook his head at Mitchell, sending a chill up Nikki's spine along with an unmistakable message: Mitchell would be next.

Undeterred, Mitchell turned back toward Finney. "The victim was scheduled to testify against Stokes in the defendant's upcoming drug trial. We had flipped Mr. Carter, promising him we would take his cooperation into account at sentencing. We have a full written confession about his involvement in a drug ring headed by Stokes, and we want to use the confession at trial, since the witness himself is no longer available. That's why we filed this motion *in limine*."

D. J. Landers rose, arms spread wide. "And we object, Your Honor, because it's classic hearsay and violates the defendant's constitutional right to confront the witnesses."

"Looks like he already did that," said Finney.

"My client was in jail when Carter died," protested Landers. "And the commonwealth doesn't have one shred of evidence that my client was involved in his death. You can't try a man for drug offenses based on written statements from dead witnesses."

"You can when the defendant orders their death," snapped Mitchell, still standing like a marine in front of his counsel table. "You waive your right to confront your witnesses when you kill them—"

"*If* you kill them," interrupted Landers. "Which, of course, didn't happen here." He turned to Mitchell. "You think my client killed your witness? File murder charges."

Mitchell didn't respond, his stare saying what words could not. Nikki knew that Mitchell had been criticized for taking cases too personally. It's what she liked about him—passion.

"You won't indict him for murder, because you don't have any evidence," Landers continued. His air of self-satisfaction curdled Nikki's stomach. "So why don't you spend your time looking for Antoine Carter's killer instead of harassing my client with this baseless drug charge?"

The muscles in Mitchell's neck tightened. "We searched the apartments of other suspected gang members. We found letters Stokes wrote from jail, telling a gang member that Antoine Carter would be testifying for the government. A few days later, Carter's dead. What more do we need?"

"Those letters, written by my client, show that he didn't believe Carter was a threat," Landers explained, his voice even. "They show my client believed that Carter would never cooperate with the government."

"Right," scoffed Mitchell. "The letters go out the week of April 4. The very next week—April 11, to be precise—Carter dies, losing his tongue in the process. What a lucky coincidence for the defendant."

Landers stiffened, fired back a retort, and the insults flew. For the next few minutes, Finney let the lawyers spar themselves out, his chin resting on his hand like a spectator at a chess match.

Finally he banged his gavel. "Gentlemen, that's enough." They both looked up at him, two schoolboys who had been prematurely untangled from a fight, seething to get back at each other.

"Let me see the letters," ordered Finney.

"I object," said Landers, his tanned face flushing.

"On what grounds?" asked Finney.

"They contain impressions of my client about his own lawyer," Landers said, crossing his arms and taking a half step away from his suddenly poisonous client. "Those allegations are untrue, and the letters themselves are privileged communications."

"Oh, come on," Mitchell blurted, obviously sensing blood. "The letters are written by a prisoner and sent to a fellow gangbanger on the outside. How can they possibly be privileged?"

"I'm just saying—," started Landers, but Finney cut him off with a wave.

"Pass 'em up," Finney said. "We'll take a brief recess while I study them. And don't worry, Mr. Landers. I'm not going to form any opinions about you based on what your client says in those letters. I'm perfectly capable of forming those judgments on my own."

"Thank you, Your Honor," said Landers, though Nikki was pretty sure the judge hadn't meant it as a compliment.

CHAPTER 3

n the judge's chambers, a messy office that reeked of cigar smoke, Nikki finished her work on the LSAT questions while Finney studied the letters. He took off his reading glasses, rubbed his forehead, and picked up the half-smoked Phillies cigar from his ashtray. Nikki glanced up and frowned her displeasure. She knew he wouldn't light up in front of her, but he still had a nasty habit of chewing on the cigar and spitting little bits and pieces into the trash can.

He cleared some phlegm from his throat and thrust the letters toward her. "Take a look at these," he said, "and let me know what you think."

"I think you ought to flush those cigars."

"About the letters," said Finney.

Nikki rose from the worn leather couch and started toward the desk.

"And let me see your answers," Finney added, pointing to the LSAT questions she had spread out on the coffee table in front of her. "If you get them all right, I'll quit cold turkey."

"Like that's going to happen," she muttered.

They traded documents, and Nikki settled back onto the couch, arranging the letters before her in chronological order. The first one, written in neat block letters from Stokes to a man nicknamed Juice, was dated April 4.

4/4/2006

Juice,

Got to get me a new mouthpiece. Landers did me greasy, wants to plead. What about that piece who repped you last year? What's his price? Landers is just yanking my chain

and rippin me off. Paid the man 15, now he's jackin me
for 10 more.
    I ain't no Trump,
    Stokes

Nikki chuckled to herself as she thought about Landers's futile
attempt to keep these letters from the court. No wonder. She loved the
phrase "did me greasy"—it perfectly described the way Landers practiced
law. She turned to the second letter, obviously written the next day.

4/5/2006

Juice,
    Word up that my man Carter's on the G-man witness list. They
say he's ready to snitch. Claim he's a gangbanger with the Black
Gangster Disciples. Ever hear of them? But Carter's ace kool. He won't drop
a dime on nobody. Carter just playin with the Man.
    Keep it real,
    Stokes

The defendant, acting like he'd never heard of the Black Gangster
Disciples, obviously had a penchant for sarcasm, thought Nikki. Still, this
letter seemed to indicate that Stokes wasn't worried about Carter's testimony, just like Landers claimed. Maybe that's because Stokes knew the
Disciples would take care of Carter before he ever made it to the stand.
    There was one more letter from Stokes.

4/6/2006 and 4/7/2006

Juice,
    Hey, my man. Bring my old lady by and tell her to bring a crate.

I'm buggin out in here and time is crawlin. BGD had a blanket
party last night for one of the new fish. As shot caller, I
had to break it up and confirm my boy was still breathin.
They punked him good.
    The Peacemaker,
    Stokes

Nikki just shook her head at this one. Even in jail, Stokes was calling
the shots, practically chuckling as his boys beat a new inmate within an
inch of his life.

The last letter was a return letter from the gangbanger named Juice,
obviously intercepted by the deputies at the jail.

4/12/2006

Stokes,
    Business is good. My suit Crankston charges $10k per count. The
man is dirty but real slick. Landers is dirty, period. Your old lady left
V-town last week for a few days. Should be back on Friday. They got
nothin on you, that's why they want to get a deal done. Don't bite.
    Juice

Nikki finished reading the letters and looked up at Finney.

"Well," he said, the cigar dangling out the side of his mouth. He held
her LSAT answers in his right hand. "Guess I'll be able to enjoy these
babies a little while longer." He licked the end of his cigar and placed it in
the ashtray, coughing as he did.

"How bad?" asked Nikki.

"One out of twelve. You would've done better if you had just put the
same letter for every question."

Nikki grunted, swallowing a few choice words for the old geezer, and shrugged. "I did that last time. You said I wasn't trying hard enough."

"It's not easy getting *less* than twenty percent right," said Finney. He leaned back in his chair, crossed his legs, and locked his hands behind his head. "What do you think?"

Nikki stacked the letters and placed them back on the judge's desk. "Guilty."

Finney raised an eyebrow.

"It's just like Mitchell said," Nikki insisted, standing in front of the judge's desk. "Stokes doesn't have to order the killing of a witness in plain English. He just has to mention to his gangbangers that one of their own is ratting him out, and they take care of the rest. You've got to allow the written statement into evidence."

"Really?"

"Yep." Nikki stood her ground and crossed her arms. She could see he wasn't buying it, but she was ready to fight for this one.

"So every time an inmate mentions a witness to someone outside the jail, and the witness later dies, we just flush the defendant's right to confront the witness in court?"

"Not every time, Judge. But here you've got proven gang connections and the timing—one week after the letter the witness is dead. And the whole tongue thing."

Finney stood and started putting his robe back on. "You'll make a good prosecutor, Nikki. But I'm not being paid to be a prosecutor. Sometimes a judge has to hold his nose and still make the right ruling, especially when a constitutional right is at stake."

"Judge," protested Nikki, following him out of his office. "You can't be serious. This guy had a gangbanger cut out the man's tongue..."

"All rise," said the deputy as Finney entered the courtroom. Nikki trailed half a step behind, veering toward her seat next to the wall. But first she made one last plea.

"His tongue, Judge. They cut out his tongue."

CHAPTER 4

In a move that surprised Nikki, Judge Finney said he would rule after he asked Detective Jenkins a few questions. He swore the witness in and took him through a series of background questions about the letters. Stokes seemed to be uninterested in the proceedings, glancing around the courtroom and occasionally sneering at the witness. Nikki couldn't believe the judge was even thinking about putting this man back on the street.

"Are you familiar with gang activity in and around the Norfolk area?" Finney asked.

"Very familiar, Judge."

"What can you tell me about the Black Gangster Disciples?"

Jenkins described the criminal activities of the Disciples in a no-nonsense tone that made him eminently believable. Under prompting from Finney, he testified about the dominating presence of the BGDs in the jails throughout the state, including the Norfolk City Jail. Many of their outside gang activities, according to the detective, were directed by leaders presently incarcerated.

"Leaders like Mr. Stokes?" asked Finney.

"Objection," called out Landers.

"Overruled."

"Yes," said the witness. "Leaders like the defendant."

"Now, take a look at that third letter sent by Mr. Stokes," instructed Finney.

While Jenkins studied the handwritten note, the defendant glared at the witness.

"What's the date on top of that letter?"

The detective hesitated. "It actually has two dates: April 6, 2006, and April 7, 2006."

"Does that strike you as unusual?" asked Finney. The judge's tone caught Nikki's attention.

The detective stared at the letter for a moment. "I'm not sure what you mean, Judge."

Finney leaned back in his swivel chair, twirling his glasses. "Well, it seems to me that it's an awful short letter to take two days to write. Maybe—what?—five total lines?"

"I guess so."

"Detective, read that letter into the record. And tell me if it sounds like the kind of letter that was actually written over the course of two days."

" 'Hey, my man. Bring my old lady by and tell her to bring a crate…,'" Jenkins read. As the detective worked his way through the letter, Finney caught Nikki's eye and graced her with a wink.

When Jenkins finished, he looked up at the judge. "Short letter," he said. "Seems to me like it was all written at the same time."

"The same thing I thought when I first read it," said Finney, looking at the defendant. "So I started asking myself, 'What's going on with the dates?' "

At this, Stokes whispered something angrily to Landers. Landers shook his head without looking at his client. In response, Stokes whispered again, angrier than before, jabbing a finger at a legal pad.

"So here's what I want you to do," said Finney. "Start with the first letter and assume that the date is more than just a date. In fact, assume that the date is an encryption key to help you decipher what these letters are really saying."

The detective studied the first letter and looked up at the judge, still confused.

"For example," continued Finney, "just for the fun of it. If the date is 4/4/2006, go to the fourth line of the message and the fourth word of that line and write it down. Then for the next letter, which I believe is dated 4/5/2006, go to the fourth line and write down the fifth word. Then for the last letter, dated 4/6/2006 and 4/7/2006, write down both the sixth and seventh words of the fourth line. Then use the same method on the reply letter. Does that make sense?"

The detective nodded, already working on his task. Landers and Stokes argued in loud whispers, and Nikki could feel a motion for a change in legal counsel coming. Mitchell turned and glanced at Nikki, the glint of victory in his pupils. And Finney, the smartest judge Nikki had ever known, sat impassively watching the detective, as if nothing more were at stake than the answers to an LSAT question.

"Okay," said the detective, working hard to maintain his professional demeanor. "I think I've got it."

"What does it say?" asked Finney.

"We object, Your Honor," said Landers, though Nikki could tell his heart wasn't in it.

"On what grounds?"

"Uh…this is total speculation. And highly prejudicial."

At this, Finney actually grinned. "How do you know it's prejudicial, Counsel? The detective hasn't even read it yet."

Stokes grabbed the arm of Landers, causing the lawyer to bend over so Stokes could unleash another tirade into his reddened ear. Landers shook it off and rose again to face Finney. "We have to assume it is, Your Honor, based on the tone of your questions."

"Overruled," snapped Finney.

Landers sat down.

The detective looked to the judge for permission to proceed.

"Go ahead," said Finney.

"Here's what I get when I apply the methodology you suggested," said the proud detective. "Stokes's letters say: 'Off Carter and confirm.' The reply of Juice, one day after Carter's murder, simply says: 'Done.'"

Finney stroked his chin and studied Stokes and Landers. After a painfully long wait, he spoke into the silence. "Another amazing coincidence, Mr. Landers?" He paused until the silence became uncomfortable. "I'm not only going to allow the confession of Antoine Carter to be submitted as evidence in the drug case, but I'm also going to suggest that Mr. Taylor seek that murder indictment you mentioned earlier."

Stokes suddenly bolted to his feet, shackles and all, causing the deputy to stand up and place a hand on her gun. "I want a new lawyer," the defendant spit out. "One who's not always stoned."

"Sit down!" Finney barked.

Stokes glared at the judge, then flopped back into his seat.

"You'll get a new lawyer," said Finney. "But no more pen pals. I'm ordering the defendant held in solitary confinement pending trial. No mail privileges, no visitation."

Then Finney turned his attention to a crestfallen Landers. "And if I were you, Counsel, I think I'd watch my tongue."

CHAPTER 5

Wow!" Nikki said when she and Finney retreated to his chambers. "How'd you figure that out?" She had grabbed the letters from the judge's bench on her way in and was even now counting the words.

"Elementary, my dear Watson."

"Huh?"

Finney shook his head. "It's Cryptology 101. These inmates all think they're Einsteins, but the code in those letters is as basic as it gets."

Nikki watched as Finney walked over to his bookshelf and pulled down a small hardback with a brown parchmentlike cover and maroon lettering. The cover featured a ghosted picture of Christ wearing a crown of thorns. Finney handed it to Nikki. "Ever see this before?"

The book was entitled *The Cross Examination of Jesus Christ*, written by some guy Nikki had never heard of. She flipped through a few pages. "I don't think so," she said.

"Not many people have." Finney gave her a cockeyed smile, then grabbed his Bible off the corner of his desk. The black leather cover was tattered and well worn. Nikki had caught him reading it on a few occasions.

As the judge searched for the right page, he started in with one of his coughing fits. He turned his head, covered his mouth, and hacked like he might spit his lungs out at any moment. Eventually he stopped coughing and started turning pages again as if nothing had happened. "Did you know that the Old Testament scribes encrypted a few words in the biblical text using a Hebrew substitution code called the *atbash* cipher?"

"Uh, no. But I'm not exactly a Bible scholar," Nikki admitted. "I think I did hear something about Bible codes once, though."

"I'm not talking about that nonsense," said Finney. "Here." He rotated the Bible for Nikki to see. "Jeremiah 25:26. See that word 'Sheshach'?"

Nikki nodded.

"That's really a Hebrew code word for Babel, or Babylon, produced using the *atbash* cipher. Someday I'll show you how it works."

"Thrilling," Nikki mumbled.

The judge put the Bible back on his desk and reached for *The Cross Examination of Jesus Christ.* "I wrote this book," he said, taking it from Nikki. "I used a pen name because a lot of people might think it inappropriate for a sitting judge to be writing a religious book like this." He opened the book to the introduction. "It's tells how Jesus handled the hostile questions of the lawyers, the Pharisees, and ultimately Pontius Pilate. You ought to read it sometime."

Nikki didn't know what to say. She knew that her judge was a religious man, but she had been working for him almost a year and never realized he had written a book. "Sounds interesting."

"Oh, it is." Finney's eyes sparkled with mischief, and he became more animated. "Christ's answers are masterful on so many levels. Every time you think you've got Him figured out, there's another whole layer you're completely missing. So I decided to add an element to the book to symbolize that."

"Of course," said Nikki, trying to remember how they had started talking about this. "Which is?"

"I've encrypted hidden messages in the book," responded Finney. "I figured if the Old Testament scribes could get away with it, so could I. Like this one in the introduction. See these hidden letters?"

Nikki looked at where the judge was pointing. She probably wouldn't have noticed the small letters on her own. But even now, as Finney pointed

out the faded images that seemed like part of the page design, it looked
like a haphazard jumble of meaningless letters, like trying to figure out
who was sitting where on the bus all over again. "I don't get it," she said
after enough time had passed so the judge would think she had tried.

Unfortunately, he picked that moment for another coughing spasm.
When he finished, his eyes watering, he handed the book back to her.
"Figure it out and I'll buy you lunch," he announced.

Don't hold your breath, Nikki thought, though you couldn't really speak
that way to a judge. "You're not going to tell me?"

"Nope. I don't give away my secrets. I just wanted you to see this so
you'd know why Stokes's method was mere child's play."

Now Nikki was curious. And she had zero chance of figuring it out
on her own. "Why would you go to all the trouble to hide these messages
in your book and not tell anybody what they mean? What if nobody figures them out?"

"Somebody will." Finney plopped down in his desk chair, looking
tired from his coughing fits. He placed his cigar in the ashtray. "John Wesley once said that there are things hidden so deeply in Scripture that future
generations will always be drawing out new truths. In some small way, I
wanted this book to symbolize that—hidden truths yet to be discovered
by future generations."

Nikki paused to think about that, struck by the effort the judge had
put into these codes. In some ways the codes were like the judge himself.
A family man who never reconciled with his son. An outspoken Christian
who wouldn't stop smoking. A puzzle. A walking contradiction. "Really,
Judge? That's why you did this?"

"Nah," said Finney. "Actually, I just like puzzles."

CHAPTER 6

The Honorable Lester Madison Banks III did not look so high and mighty as he sat naked in his Jacuzzi, his eyes bugged out with fear at what he saw on the small monitor on the bathroom counter. In fact, to the Assassin, the sixty-six-year-old judicial despot looked more like a prune than a powerful state court judge. Except that the old man's wrinkled skin was pasty white, the only purple coming from his shivering lips and the round Gorbachev birthmark on the front half of His Honor's mostly bald scalp.

"Pronounce the sentence," demanded an anxious voice into the Assassin's earpiece. The Client. Someone the Assassin detested even more than the judge shivering with fear in front of him. A control freak. Consumed by revenge. With only one redeeming quality.

Money. One point two million, to be exact. For a high-risk hit involving a judge, one million dollars. For the privilege of watching via videophone, an extra two hundred thousand.

The Assassin kept his gun leveled at the judge though he knew it was no longer necessary. "Remind him how merciful we're being," the Client's voice continued with a mixture of stridency and delight. "We're sparing his grandchildren and will be executing him in a certifiably humane fashion."

"I'll stick with the script," the Assassin said in return. He should never have allowed this guy to monitor the execution. Even by the Assassin's standards, the Client was bizarre.

"I want to watch him die," the Client had insisted when he first hired the Assassin. He asked to actually come along, as if this were some kind of theme-park ride that he could enjoy while sitting next to the Assassin. The Assassin vetoed the idea but, for the extra cash, agreed to bring along the videophone device that now sat on the bathroom counter, transmitting every moan and grimace from the embattled judge.

Next to the camera sat a small monitor, the sole reason the judge had earlier gone from being demanding and arrogant, even at gunpoint, to being compliant as a whipped puppy. The monitor showed a real-time video of the judge's youngest grandson, sleeping blissfully in his own house, less than half a mile from the judge's home. The young boy was barely distinguishable in a room illuminated only by an Aslan nightlight.

After the Assassin bragged that he had planted an explosive device that could be detonated by remote control (a small but necessary lie), His Honor became very good at following orders.

Banks had disrobed and filled the Jacuzzi with water just as the Assassin instructed. Before climbing in, the judge turned on the bathroom television, located on a custom-designed wooden shelf above the Jacuzzi. The judge seemed to shrink as he slid into the water, the FOX News commentators babbling in the background.

"He looks pitiful," the Client said, as if the Assassin needed a running commentary. Ignoring him, the Assassin recited the indictment against the judge. In a steady monotone, the Assassin reminded the judge of the most egregious mistake of His Honor's celebrated judicial career. It had cost a young woman her life. And now it was time to pay. An eye for an eye. A tooth for a tooth. A life for a life.

He pronounced the old man guilty and asked Judge Banks if he had any final words. But the judge didn't answer, keeping his eyes glued instead to the monitor showing his grandson. The judge seemed to be drawing strength from the image of the boy.

"Not even an apology," sneered the Client.

Which made the Assassin respect the judge, if only a little. But the Assassin still had a job to do.

"Before I carry out the sentence, Your Honor, my client wants me to remind you of your own opinion, twelve years ago, in *State v. Vincent,* when you delivered a stirring defense of the constitutionality of the electric chair. Do you remember that case, Judge?"

His Honor ignored the question.

"You want your grandson to survive this?" the Assassin asked, his voice flat.

Banks nodded, still transfixed by the monitor.

"Then answer the question. Do you remember the case?"

"Yes."

"You ruled that the electric chair was not cruel and unusual, right?"

"That's correct."

"Do you remember the testimony of the doctor hired by Mr. Vincent's lawyers?"

The judge shuddered, perhaps at the thought of the testimony, perhaps at the specter of his own impending death. He took a furtive glance at the Assassin and then turned back to the monitor, breathing sporadically.

"Make him answer," the Client demanded. But the Assassin tuned out the voice in his earpiece.

"The doctor testified that death by electrocution is an extremely violent and painful affair," the Assassin said. "He testified about watching an inmate squirm as he died in the chair, the veins on the inmate's neck standing out like steel bands. He said the temperature of the brain would have approached the boiling point of water and that when the coroner performed the post-electrocution autopsy, the liver was so hot it couldn't be touched by human hands. Do you remember all that, Judge?"

His Honor gave the slightest, smallest nod. The imperial power of the bench reduced to this—a shriveled and trembling old man.

"How did you rule, Judge?"

Silence. But the Assassin didn't have time to wait him out.

"How did you rule?" he asked more sharply.

"I rejected the defendant's motion."

The Assassin took a step toward the television. Two days ago he had broken into Banks's home and replaced the GFCI outlet with a faulty one that wouldn't trip the circuit when the water seeped into the high-voltage block on the back of the picture tube. Thirty thousand volts. He had replaced a few other outlets as well, so it would look like a case of faulty wiring, and he loosened the screws on the wooden brace supporting the television shelf to complete the accident scenario.

All of this, he knew, would be considered entirely too coincidental for the city's homicide detectives. But the Assassin believed in redundancy— a belt *and* suspenders approach—so he left two false leads. The detectives would pride themselves in ruling out an accidental death and suspecting foul play. But then they would immediately focus their investigation on the La Familia gang, concluding that this was a retaliatory strike for the contemptuous way Banks had sentenced a gang leader to death just last week. It was retaliatory, all right. But who would suspect an eight-year-old case?

An eye for an eye. Wait until a judge crosses a gang noted for violence and you can literally get away with murder.

The Assassin placed his free hand on top of the television and stared down at the judge. "You still believe the electric chair is not cruel and unusual?"

"Don't hurt my grandson. Please."

The Assassin felt a small pang of sympathy but quickly extinguished it. He had learned to suppress every emotion. "I've got no desire to harm the boy, Judge. Provided you're ready to face your death sentence like a man."

"Don't tell him that," the Client hissed into the earpiece. "That's not in the script. He needs to die wondering."

"You know, Judge," the Assassin continued, "they say that when Jesse Tafero was executed in Florida, witnesses saw him clench his fists and convulse for about four minutes while smoke and sparks shot out of his death mask. Something about the sponges on his head not being properly placed." There was more, but the Assassin was suddenly weary of this scripted approach to the old man's death. The Client was sick. The judge just needed to die.

"Any last words?" asked the Assassin. He placed his hand firmly on top of the television, preparing to send it and the shelf crashing into the Jacuzzi.

"What are you doing?" the Client asked. "That's not the end."

Without warning, the judge gasped and clutched at his chest. His eyes went wide as he convulsed and jerked back in the Jacuzzi, fighting for air. "Push the television!" the Client barked. "Push the television!"

But the Assassin pressed the End Call button on his cell phone, turned his back on the thrashing judge, and walked calmly over to the bathroom counter. He powered down the video monitor of the judge's grandson and the video feed for the Client. When he looked back over his shoulder, the judge had stopped moving, slipping peacefully down the side of the Jacuzzi, all but his head and shoulders submerged in the water.

A heart attack. Fate had intervened and spared the judge the electric chair. The La Familia scapegoat wouldn't be necessary. The Assassin began the tedious process of sanitizing the crime scene, focusing on the work at hand while trying to keep the guilt and emotions at bay. But the Assassin knew the emotions would eventually catch up with him. Only Hollywood hit men feel no remorse. In real life, the emotions eventually bubble to the surface.

Like the last job. A true family man. Two days after the killing, the nightmares started. The Assassin almost lost his mind, saved by prescription drugs and a new job that demanded total focus. This one.

Now, to preserve his sanity, he would immediately begin focusing on the precision planning required for the next job. One last high-profile hit and another big payday. Afterward, he could put this behind him forever. It was only fitting that his final assignment would be the most complicated and daring of his entire career, making Judge Banks's carefully orchestrated death seem like child's play. The elaborate machinery of death for the Assassin's final unsuspecting victim was already well under construction.

CHAPTER 7

Oliver Finney felt ridiculous. A grown man, sitting in a big New York conference room straight off the set of *The Apprentice*. He was the only one wearing a sports coat and tie; these television folks all dressed like a bunch of burglars—black on black. At the time he applied for a slot on *Faith on Trial*, it had seemed like a good idea. But he never really dreamed he'd be sitting here...

"We really like the idea of a judge on this show representing the Christian faith," said the man in the middle on the opposite side of the table. In Finney's mind the guy fit to a T the stereotype for a director—like maybe this guy had himself been selected by central casting. The man pulled his gray hair back in a ponytail and looked over wire-rimmed glasses at Finney. He had on a ratty black T-shirt that covered a soft little gut but exposed two skinny arms and one forearm tattoo. He wore a left earring so everybody would know he wasn't completely out of touch with the younger culture. The others in the room all nodded vigorously when he spoke, as if their jobs depended on it.

"Christians are always complaining about the judges who run this country," the director continued. What was his name? Something McCormack—Bruce or Barry or one of those B names—but a little different. Finney had never been good with names. "Now they'll be cheering for one."

The room became quiet for a moment as the production team considered the delicious irony they were about to foist on Christians everywhere. A young woman at the end of the table practically smacked her lips while McCormack finished shuffling through Finney's application. He put the papers down and stared at Finney for a moment—a director's feeble attempt at intimidation, Finney supposed.

"You're my first choice, Judge. But I've got a couple of concerns. My first has to do with your reasons for being on this show. Your application is not entirely clear."

"Other than a million dollars for my favorite charity?" Finney asked. But they both knew that wasn't the reason.

"Yes. Other than that."

Finney slid forward in his seat. The situation called for blunt honesty, his specialty. "When you sit where I sit and see what I see, you get concerned about the next generation." Finney surveyed the group, practically daring somebody to give him one of those patronizing media-elite smirks, the kind that try to make you feel stupid for defending traditional values. "Gang rapes. Crack heads. Last week I sentenced a fifteen-year-old kid for stabbing another kid thirty-seven times with a Phillips head screwdriver. The victim was fourteen."

Finney let out an exasperated breath. Even talking about this could be depressing, the relentless march of wasted lives. "You know how many of the kids that I've sentenced in the past two months have fathers living at home?" he asked McCormack.

The director shook his head. "Not many?"

"Try none," said Finney. "Not one time did I have a father come to court and stand up for these fifteen- and sixteen-year-old kids. So what do I do? Hand down long prison sentences. Warehouse more and more of these kids in places where they learn how to become career criminals. Somehow we've got to break this chain. Somehow we've got to reach these kids. Maybe a few of them will watch this show. God knows, most of them will never set foot in church."

Finney realized he had silenced the room with his sanctimonious lecture, but he didn't care. McCormack had asked the question. Finney was too old and too sick to worry about what other people might think.

McCormack jotted a few notes while the silence hung in the air. "Fair enough," he said when he had finished. "Which leads me to the second issue." He paused, apparently at a loss about how best to phrase this. "It says here you've got metastatic lung cancer."

The "c" word sucked the remaining air out of the room. Though they all knew the facts, McCormack's saying it out loud made the youngsters stare at Finney as if he were already a ghost.

So Finney decided it was time to loosen things up a little. The last several months had taught him how awkward it could be for healthy people to be around a cancer patient. "Oh," Finney said, glancing around, "I must have the wrong show. I didn't know I'd stumbled into the WWE studio."

Nobody grinned. "It's not championship wrestling," said McCormack matter-of-factly, "but it's not *Jeopardy!* either. *Faith on Trial* will test you spiritually, intellectually, emotionally"—he paused so the point would not be lost on Finney—"and physically."

"Such as?"

"You know I can't provide details."

Finney was tired of playing games. He wasn't accustomed to meetings he didn't control. And he felt another coughing fit coming on.

"Is it something a fifty-nine-year-old cancer patient can do or not?" he asked.

The director hesitated for a second or two, just long enough to convey his concern. "I think so."

"Then where do I sign?"

McCormack looked to his left and his right. Nobody registered an objection. "Congratulations, Judge Finney," he said, sliding a sheaf of papers across the table. "It looks like the future of Christianity is resting squarely on your shoulders."

"Thanks," said Finney, though the word was cut short by a cough. He put his fist over his mouth and hacked away while the others watched wide eyed as if he might kick the bucket at any minute.

"I think it's getting better," Finney said.

⁓

The paperwork was preposterous. According to the documents, Finney released the show, the producers, and anybody associated with the enterprise from any and all claims of whatsoever kind or nature. There was a full page listing all the dire consequences that would develop, including lawsuits for injunctions and a two-million-dollar liquidated damages payment, if the contestants divulged any information about the show's results before all of the episodes had aired.

The release went on for pages, explaining all the dangers facing the participants and all the reasons they couldn't sue the show—not for injury or death or fraud or deception or breach of contract or loss of consortium. Finney laughed out loud at the last one. "Loss of consortium" would be the loss of a spouse's companionship and physical affections due to an injury. Some New York lawyer obviously had too much time on his hands. Finney had been a widower for several years.

"Is this a reality show or a POW camp?" Finney asked.

"Lawyers," McCormack said as if that explained everything.

Finney skimmed quickly through the boilerplate, content in the knowledge that most of this stuff wouldn't hold up in court anyway. He flipped to the end and found the place for his signature.

"You don't want to read it?" asked McCormack.

"I know what it says," Finney responded. Actually, he was rushing to sign because he felt yet another coughing spell coming on. "Basically, I'm signing my life away."

McCormack's mouth formed a thin line, and he didn't say a word. He didn't have to. Finney had spent the last twenty years reading the eyes of witnesses. Compared to the cons Finney dealt with on a daily basis, McCormack was an open book.

You have no idea, McCormack was saying.

CHAPTER 8

We lost the rabbi?" Cameron Murphy repeated in disbelief. The executive producer of *Faith on Trial* ran his fingers through close-cropped brown hair, then subconsciously rubbed the stubble of his beard. "How can we lose a rabbi?" He stood and shook his head. "What else can we mess up? This is our last preproduction meeting, folks. We've got one week. One week!" He cursed through clenched teeth.

Everyone around the table except Bryce McCormack winced. Bryce had known Murphy too well for too long. He had known the producer would explode when he learned the news. In fact, Bryce had secretly counted down the seconds as the casting assistant stammered through the news. *Liftoff,* he thought just as Murphy exploded.

Halfway down the conference table, the assistant casting director spoke softly. "The Anti-Defamation League got to him," she said. "They've been making a lot of noise about how inappropriate this show is—fosters competition and hate among religions, the Jews have suffered enough from religious bigotry, that type of thing. Rabbi Demsky wanted some assurances we couldn't give him."

"Like what?" sputtered Murphy. "What was he asking?"

The young woman fumbled through her notes for a second. McCormack thought about bailing her out but decided against it. If she planned on being the lead director someday, she'd have to learn how to take the heat. "Not allowing the contestants to denigrate one another's faiths. No proselytizing people of other faiths. Plus, he wanted a complete dossier on the Muslim contestant—"

Murphy strung together a creative string of curse words and then apparently remembered that a fair number of the folks around the table were Jewish. He shook his head and stood to get a refill on his coffee. "Why didn't he just ask to direct the show? We could have given him Bryce's job." Murphy reached the counter and poured himself a cup. "This is reality TV, not a scholarly symposium at the Guggenheim."

Murphy returned to his seat without further profanity (a minor miracle) and turned to the assistant casting director again. "Who's the backup?"

"Rabbi David Cohen," the woman said hopefully. She passed a file down the table to Murphy. "Rabbinical studies at Hebrew University. Law degree from Columbia."

"And how do we know the Anti-Defamation League won't get to him?"

"We don't know for sure. But he doesn't seem the type to be intimidated by anybody."

Murphy took a sip of black coffee and glanced through the file. "I remember this guy," he said tersely. "Too old. We've already got the judge and that Buddha dude. We don't need another old guy." He shot a look at Bryce, who stared back over wire-rimmed glasses. Bryce was two years older but hadn't aged as well as Murphy, a fact that Murphy brought up whenever possible. Unlike Murphy, Bryce let nature take its course—no hair color, no plastic surgery, no LASIK surgery. The cumulative effects cost him the appearance of ten years. "No offense, McCormack."

Bryce McCormack showed Murphy his middle finger. He was one of the few folks around the table who could get away with it.

The assistant slid another file toward Murphy. "Levi Katz is thirty-three and an up-and-comer in a big New York law firm. A little weak on religious studies but very camera friendly."

Camera friendly. A euphemism for young and good looking, words that nobody used for fear of getting sued. Except for Murphy. After all, he was the producer. Laws for mere mortals didn't apply to him. Murphy glanced at the young Levi Katz's picture.

"What'd you think of this guy?" he asked Bryce.

"Orthodox Jew," Bryce said, sounding bored. "Serious about his faith. I don't remember what skeletons he had in his closet."

Murphy checked the file. "Fooled around on his wife," Murphy said. "Don't we already have one of those?"

Bryce hitched a shoulder. "It could still serve its purpose."

Murphy didn't look convinced. "What kind of medical condition does this Levi Katz have?" he asked, flipping through the file again. "All I see in here is a blood condition he's taking medication for. How does that qualify as life threatening?"

This time the casting assistant was barely audible. "That's all he's got, Mr. Murphy."

Murphy sighed, a signal that these people could never get anything right. "That won't work," he barked. "A life-threatening medical condition—we've had that requirement in place from day one."

The table grew silent. The casting crew were apparently fresh out of Jewish candidates with life-threatening medical conditions, theological training, a shameful secret, and if possible, a legal background.

For the next half hour, they discussed whether to do the show with three older contestants or to conduct an expedited search for a suitable replacement. It was Bryce McCormack who finally came up with an idea that could turn this setback into ratings gold. The *Passion* principle, he called it—a lesson from the extraordinary success of *The Passion of the Christ.* "Embrace the controversy," he lectured. "Tell the world that we won't back down. We believe in a free marketplace of religion with no rules that would interfere with a robust debate. But just to show what great egalitarians we are, we will agree to give Rabbi Demsky five full minutes on our first show to tell the world why they shouldn't watch us."

Heads turned toward McCormack as if he'd lost his mind. Who had ever heard of such a thing? But they all had to admit that embracing the controversy had worked for Mel Gibson.

Before the meeting was over, they agreed to recommend it to the suits. "I hope you know what you're doing," Murphy said to Bryce after the others had dispersed.

"Controversy," said Bryce, smiling like a madman, "is a reality show's best friend."

❧

The Assassin checked and rechecked the final punch list Friday night. Professional killers don't operate on emotion or instinct. They plan. Then they check every detail of the plan. Twice. Then they execute, pushing aside every emotion. Otherwise, they don't survive.

He had survived the last job better than most others in his profession would have. The coroner had ruled the death accidental. The Assassin had even thought about going to the funeral, but he knew investigators would be there surveying the crowd. The mental images of the old man croaking in the Jacuzzi had lasted only a few weeks. Soon the Assassin was consumed with planning his next job, sweating over every detail and developing backup plans for every contingency.

That's why the Assassin's services didn't come cheap. The down payment for the *Faith on Trial* job had already been confirmed. He would get five hundred thousand dollars up front, wired to an offshore bank. The Assassin would transfer the funds at least three times before they reached their final destination. Another two hundred thousand would come once the Assassin reached the island. The rest of the money—eight hundred thousand—would be paid after the successful hit.

The total of one-point-five million dollars, though it might sound like a lot of money to most people, was actually low for a job like this. High exposure meant high risk. And what could generate more exposure than death on a high-profile reality show? A federal investigation would follow. After the job, the Assassin would have to undergo a complete makeover—nose, chin, eyes, hair, weight, everything. Plus, the expenses would be substantial.

But the Assassin wasn't complaining about his fee. After all, one-point-five million dollars was more than the prize money for the winner's charity of choice.

The Assassin would earn every penny.

PART 2

CONTESTANTS

*Strive mightily, but eat
and drink as friends.*
—SHAKESPEARE

*No wise combatant underestimates
their antagonist.*
—JOHANN WOLFGANG VON GOETHE

CHAPTER 9

A *t least the show is transporting us in style,* Finney thought. He climbed on board the network's Gulfstream IV with the other *Faith on Trial* contestants, preparing to leave Teterboro Airport in New Jersey for a top-secret set location that the producers took great pains to conceal. Cameron Murphy joined them a few minutes later.

He introduced himself to the contestants and collected watches, cell phones, computers, and PDAs. He cleared his throat and made a few curious announcements.

"You've got a long flight ahead of you, so relax and get some sleep," he said, looking from one contestant to the next. "You're going to need it.

"We'll explain the official rules of the game when we're on location, during our first day of shooting, which is when the game starts. However, from this point on, pretty much everything you do or say will be recorded on camera. You need to wear your microphones at all times, except when you're sleeping or in the bathroom." As Murphy spoke, a couple of cameras were already running, one focused on him and one scanning the contestants. "Everything we catch on film is fair game for the show. And I do mean *everything.*"

At this, Murphy looked at the younger contestants, including a young female scientist named Victoria Kline. She had introduced herself to Finney with a firm handshake and a hard gaze. Apparently, Murphy felt no need to lecture Finney about extracurricular activity.

"While we're shooting, you'll be prohibited from interacting with camera or audio crews or your director, Bryce McCormack, or myself. It will feel awkward at first, but after a while, you'll get used to ignoring us and you'll feel like the cameras are not even there."

Murphy hesitated for a moment, as if he wasn't sure how to phrase this next part. "As you know, you'll be required to defend your faith over the next two weeks, and I think all of you will be very persuasive. But you need to know that *Faith on Trial* is not just about defending your faith; it's also about living your faith under the most stressful circumstances imaginable. So if you're not ready to do that…this is your last chance to opt out."

None of the contestants moved, including Finney. He knew how reality shows worked. He would be ready for anything they threw at him.

"I'm scheduled to leave on another plane a little later, so I'll see you on location," Murphy said. "I'm not going to ask if you've got questions because I know you've got a ton of questions I can't answer. That's something you'll just have to get used to."

The man had an arrogance that Finney didn't like. What was it with these TV people? A cocky producer. A surly director. And Finney thought lawyers were bad!

Murphy turned toward the door, but Finney blurted out his question anyway. "Is this a nonsmoking flight?"

Victoria groaned and the others looked at Finney as if he'd just proposed a suicide mission.

"Yes, Judge Finney. I'm afraid it is."

∽

At forty-one thousand feet, Finney met his match in the person of the young man sitting across from him—Skyler Hadji, or Swami Skyler Hadji, as the kid called himself. Finney almost laughed when they first shook hands. The guy couldn't have been a day over thirty. With his shaggy blond hair, light blue eyes, slender build, and serious tan, the "Swami" had California surfer dude written all over him.

"I'm not a real swami," he confessed almost in a whisper. "It's just a nickname my friends gave me."

Turns out the Swami was the chosen advocate for Hinduism, a passionate convert who embraced the faith after his acting career hit the rocks. He legally changed his name and traveled to India for two years to study with a leader of the Bhakti sect of Hinduism, then returned to California enlightened and focused. He attended the University of Southern California Law School and graduated near the top of his class. His goal, he said, was to represent the workers in India being abused by corporate America. As soon as he won this reality show.

After a few hours of boredom on the flight, the Swami suggested a few hands of Texas hold 'em. He talked two cameramen into playing and, after the other contestants refused, Judge Finney as well.

A half hour later, the chips were piled high in front of the Swami, who always seemed to know just when to hold and when to bet. Finney started chewing on the stub of a cigar, but it was apparently no match for the Swami's serious card karma, as he called it. Though Finney was losing, he couldn't help but like this kid. The other contestants seemed to be taking themselves seriously, but the Swami was obviously intent on going with the flow.

"All but one," said Finney as he pushed a large pile of chips to the middle of the table. The two cameramen each raised an eyebrow and folded, but the Swami barely moved. He closed his eyes, cards held in front of him, and hummed in a low voice. He uttered Vishnu's name a few times—something he had done on every major hand ("You ought to try it, Judge O")—and then opened his eyes to glance at Finney and the cameraman standing behind Finney, one of two who had been filming the entire game.

The Swami smiled and started counting Finney's chips. "I'll call," he said, shoving a big pile of his own chips to the middle of the table, "and raise you one." Finney flicked his last chip in as well. The only reason he had held it back in the first place was so that the Swami would have to reveal his cards first. It would make the look on the kid's face that much sweeter.

Finney liked his chances. There were five cards showing on the table: two aces, a jack, a ten and a deuce. In his hand Finney held another ten and a useless six, meaning that the Swami would have to beat two pairs— aces over tens—or lose the biggest hand of the night.

The Swami laid down the cards in his hand—two *queens*. His aces and queens were more than a match for Finney's hand. The Swami raised an eyebrow and shrugged. "You've been a good sport, Judge O."

But before Finney could reveal his own hand, he started coughing. He pulled the cigar out of his mouth and placed it on the table, covering his mouth with his free hand as he turned his head and hacked. His other hand, the one holding his cards, dropped down near his lap.

"You okay?" the Swami asked. "I'm not real good at CPR."

"Fine, fine," said Finney as he brought the coughing under control. He cleared his throat a few times. "Where were we?"

The Swami pointed to the table. "You were just about to concede defeat, Judge O."

"Oh yeah," said Finney. He laid down the cards in his hand. An ace and a ten! A miraculous full house. The useless six was nowhere in sight.

"Whoa," said one of the cameramen.

"Nice play, Judge O," said the Swami. Finney had just outcheated the Swami, and the Swami knew it. But the Swami's face gave nothing away, not even a flicker of surprise or annoyance.

As the Swami started shuffling for the next hand, Finney smiled and 'fessed up. "I can't take your money," he said, pulling the six of hearts from under his leg and placing it on the table. "When I figured out that you were looking into that camera over my shoulder and reading my cards, I slipped an ace out of the deck and waited for just the right hand."

The Swami matched Judge Finney's smile with his own, a much brighter smile with the perfectly aligned teeth of an actor. "I know," said the Swami. "You pulled it out four hands ago."

Finney tried not to show his own surprise. And it was at that moment, looking directly into the Swami's eyes, that Judge Oliver G. Finney knew he would be up against a formidable opponent in the days ahead.

"I was still planning on making a little comeback, Judge O, before we called it a day."

Then, still smiling, the Swami reached down next to his own leg and placed a pair of kings on the table.

"Whoa," said the cameraman again.

"Sometimes Vishnu needs a little help," explained the Swami.

CHAPTER 10

Though he had plenty of time, Finney had less luck getting to know the other contestants. They were not exactly the kind of folks you'd invite to a cocktail party. The Muslim advocate, Kareem Hasaan, seemed determined not to let friendship get in the way of victory. It appeared to Finney that the show's producers had intentionally played into the stereotype of the combative and foreboding Muslim. Kareem was the largest of the five contestants, a good two or three inches taller than Finney, with ripped muscles that made his black T-shirt look like a Batman costume. Finney guessed the man was about thirty-five, with thick and curly black hair and the dark features of the Lebanese—the identity of his native country was one of the few things Kareem had disclosed during the plane ride.

"Isn't that where the Hezbollah are from?" whispered the Swami.

But the other thing Finney learned about Kareem didn't seem to fit the stereotype. He described himself as a "human-rights lawyer," representing clients who had been discriminated against, including criminal defendants. A Muslim human-rights lawyer. It made about as much sense as a cigar-smoking judge representing Christianity.

If Hasaan won the award for intensity, Dr. Victoria Kline won the prize for aloofness.

"What religion do you represent?" asked Finney.

"None," replied Dr. Kline.

Finney waited for further elaboration but none came. "All right then," said Finney. "Wonder what movie they're showing on this flight?"

"I'm a scientist, Judge Finney," Kline replied. "I'll be advocating the position of science, not religion."

"Didn't know they were mutually exclusive." Finney said it with a smile, but a thin one.

"Let's leave the advocacy for the show, shall we?" Kline asked.

"It's a good thing she's pretty," the Swami whispered later. " 'Cause she doesn't stand a chance at Miss Congeniality."

The final contestant seemed to fit the mold of his religion better than anyone else. Dr. Hokoji Ando, a bald Asian with heavy glasses, couldn't have been more than five foot six. "A pint-sized Buddha," according to the Swami, who claimed he'd never seen a Buddhist priest so thin. Though Ando walked with a distinct limp, he still managed to carry himself with a soft-spoken dignity that oozed wisdom. He was the one person on the show older than Finney, though Finney would have bet his life savings on the fact that Ando would live longer. *Those Eastern guys never smoke, and they eat all that seaweed,* thought Finney. Ando could live to be a hundred.

Most of the trip, Dr. Ando sat alone and meditated.

Not to be outdone, Finney stared out the window and prayed. He prayed for God's will in this game—a noble prayer but also one he knew would mean victory for his cause. When he finished praying, Finney pondered again his reasons for doing this. The whole experience still seemed so surreal. But he was committed now and knew there was no turning back.

What he had said to McCormack and the others was true—Finney hoped this show might be a vehicle to reach a few members of the next generation. But he had other motivations as well. Part of it was the intrigue. Finney liked nothing better than the competition of a challenging intellectual problem, and what could beat this? But it was more than that. Finney was tired of seeing Christianity represented by those who gave Jesus a bad name. Screaming televangelists. Judgmental legalists. Uncommitted believers who shirked the tough sayings of Christ. He believed a reformed lawyer-turned-judge like himself could do better—or at least no worse.

More important still was the updated diagnosis he'd received just a month ago. The lung cancer had metastasized to his liver. It was, Finney knew, a death sentence with no appeal. "You have six months at the out-side," his doctor said. "Maybe a year with the right kind of chemo." But Finney passed on the chemo. He wanted to make the last six months count. And that's what was really driving this; that's why he was here.

The pilot interrupted Finney's thoughts with an announcement: "Fasten your seat belts and draw your window shades." The Gulfstream was about to begin its descent. The contestants, explained the pilot, were not supposed to know where the plane was landing.

After a smooth touchdown, the pilot asked the contestants to stay seated until they received further instructions. A few minutes later, Murphy and his production crew boarded the plane. Murphy surveyed the five contestants, obviously relishing the fact that he knew what would happen next and they had no idea. Finney decided he might as well get used to it.

"I hope you had a comfortable flight," Murphy said. "Thanks for your patience. We are almost to our destination."

In his hand Murphy held several black blindfolds. He gave one to each contestant. "The location of our set needs to remain undisclosed for a number of reasons. So you'll need to put these on until we arrive."

Finney took a blindfold from the producer and felt stupid. He had signed up for a sophisticated reality show analyzing the world's great religions, not pin the tail on the donkey.

"Cool," said the Swami, snapping his on.

Kareem Hasaan frowned and turned the blindfold over in his hands as if he might quit on the spot. "Is this really necessary?" the civil-rights attorney asked, his eyes clouding over.

"I'm afraid so," said Murphy with as much authority as possible. He probably didn't expect a contestant uprising quite so early. "We'll make sure your luggage arrives safely on the island with you."

Kareem looked at the other contestants and then at Finney. Finney shrugged and pulled the elastic over his head.

"Do we get a last cigarette?" the Swami wanted to know.

Murphy thanked the contestants for their cooperation, and then some assistants helped Finney down the steps of the Gulfstream and onto the paved runway. Finney tried to look out the bottom of the mask but could see nothing. He felt the hot and sticky air of some kind of tropical island—no surprise there. The show's producers had told them to dress casually for the trip and said that the outside temperatures could reach the nineties. It felt to Finney, who was wearing jeans, a T-shirt, and his John Deere cap, as if they had underestimated by twenty degrees.

"We're going right over this way," someone said, pulling Finney along. The humid tropical air smelled like jet fuel. Unknown persons loaded Finney onto an aircraft and placed him in a seat next to someone who used too much aftershave.

"Can we take these off now?" he heard Kareem ask.

The answer, in a deep voice that Finney hadn't heard before, was a gruff "No. We'll tell you when to take them off."

Finney's seat started rumbling as an aircraft engine fired up, and he heard the whir of helicopter blades overhead. The temptation to remove his blindfold was nearly overwhelming, but Finney decided to be a good soldier and leave it on. Before long, he could feel the helicopter rising into the air.

"This is stupid," said Kareem loud enough to be heard over the roar of blades and engine. But since nobody joined in the complaining, he didn't say another word the rest of the trip.

Finney estimated that the trip took less than thirty minutes before the helicopter landed. Somebody helped Finney off the helicopter and whisked him away from the bird. This climate seemed identical to that of the last stop, perhaps a few degrees cooler. Finney felt a strong blast of wind as the helicopter took off again and then listened intently as it retreated into the distance.

The stillness engulfed him. For a moment it felt as if Finney were all alone in the warm island breeze. The sounds reminded him of the Virginia Beach inlets on a quiet summer night—the chirping of some kind of cricket, the faint rhythm of ocean waves marching to the shore, the wind rustling through the trees.

"You can remove the masks now."

Finney's eyes adjusted quickly to the light as he gaped at his new environs. Blue sky. The beautiful green hue of the ocean. White sand and palm trees a few hundred yards down the hill from the landing pad.

"Awesome!" exclaimed the Swami. "This place rocks!"

Even Kareem let a small smile crease his lips.

"Welcome to Paradise Island," said their slender host, a woman whom Finney had met before leaving New Jersey. Her name was Tammy something or other. Or it might have been Jamie; he couldn't remember. She had on a short skirt and a low-cut blouse—a sure sign that the producers intended on using this piece in the first program. Even taking into account the well-known fact that television tended to add ten pounds to a person's physique, Finney thought their host could stand to put on a few pounds and would still look just fine. A woman's collarbone should not stick out that much, in Finney's humble opinion.

Sure enough, the cameras whirred away, recording the contestants' reactions. Only Dr. Ando seemed not to be excited. He looked around with the same level of detachment you might expect from a Gold Medallion traveler surveying another Holiday Inn hotel room.

"I hope you enjoy your stay here over the next two weeks," said their host.

"What's her name again?" Finney whispered to the Swami.

"Tammy," said the Swami without taking his eyes off the woman. "Awesome name."

The director shot Finney and the Swami the same look Finney used when people whispered in court.

But Tammy didn't seem to notice. "As you know, you've each been selected—all except one of you, that is—because of your firm commitment to your faith. The nation will be watching to see how your faith stacks up when you encounter"—she paused like an amateur actress trying to manufacture drama—"trouble in paradise."

Finney thought the line was cheesy, but what did he know about television production? He did know that this moment was staged, and he hated to ruin it, but he just couldn't help himself. When you've got to cough... He tried swallowing it and choking it down, but that only made his face red and made the urge overwhelming.

He cleared his throat, turned his head and hacked away, spitting up phlegm in the process. When he stopped, all eyes and most cameras were trained on him.

"Allergies," he said.

"Let's roll that one again," said McCormack with no small amount of annoyance in his voice. "Would you guys mind putting your blindfolds back on?"

∽

It took them four takes just to get the opening scene right, and Bryce McCormack was ready to pull his hair out, long gray strand by long gray strand. Between Finney, who always picked the worst possible moment to cough, and Tammy, who overdramatized every line, the cast would turn Paradise Island into a director's worst nightmare. There were naturals in the acting business; these folks were not among them.

Tammy had been Murphy's choice, and Bryce didn't have the heart or the will to veto her. She had originally garnered her fifteen minutes of fame as a contestant on the fourth season of *The Bachelorette*. Within six months, the romance that budded on that show fell apart, and Murphy decided to give her a second shot at the spotlight. "A great gimmick," he told Bryce, "a reality-show contestant hosting another reality show."

It sounded clever at the time. But they had both been regretting it ever since. Next time, Bryce would insist on hiring a professional.

CHAPTER 11

T he next hour consisted of the Paradise tour, as Murphy dubbed it. The property consisted of several buildings, all nestled around a picturesque cove with some of the clearest ocean water Finney had ever seen. He had spent most of his adult life sailing the waters around Tidewater, Virginia, so the ocean was nothing new. But comparing the Atlantic at Virginia Beach to this body of water was like comparing his dingy Norfolk courtroom to the U.S. Supreme Court.

This was the ocean as God had originally colored it—translucent green, a color Finney had seen only on postcards. The sand along the half-mile stretch of beach was pure white, with loungers and a large Hobie Cat sailboat calling Finney's name. Two double-seated Wave Runners and a surf kayak sat next to the Hobie.

"There's a Hobie Cat, if you like to sail, as well as snorkeling gear and a kayak," Murphy said, pointing toward the shed at the end of the beach. "The snorkeling fins, masks, and life jackets are inside the shed. The kayak paddle is right next to the kayak. For safety reasons, please stay inside this large cove if you sail or kayak. The Wave Runners are reserved for our security guards."

The Swami groaned about not being able to use the Wave Runners, but the tour continued. A sidewalk and a manicured lawn connected the beach area to the main building, which contained two floors of condo units—about forty in all, by Finney's estimation. Each contestant would have his or her own condo. Pink and yellow flowers in full bloom bordered the path. The whole island was lush, its rolling volcanic hills covered in dark-green vegetation. This little resort was the only sign of civilization as far as Finney could see.

He had expected more primitive accommodations, the kind you see on *Survivor.* But this stuff was all first class—more like a converted five-star resort.

"Is this some kind of vacation property?" Finney asked.

"Like Tammy said, it's paradise," Murphy replied. "And that's about all we can tell you."

A small but stately restaurant—the Paradise View—was built on a rocky ledge that overlooked the cove. "This is the mess hall," quipped Murphy. The sun streamed through the floor-to-ceiling windows on the ocean side, and Finney could only imagine how nice this place would be at sunset in a few hours, with white linen covering the tables and the chandelier providing dim interior light.

The only place that didn't have a view was a large ballroom in the main building that the producers had converted into a library. It now had a large conference table in the middle, a few comfortable chairs and reading lamps spread around, and rows upon rows of bookshelves. Fittingly enough, it smelled musty. "We've collected nearly five thousand books on the major world religions," Murphy said proudly. "Even a few authored by the folks in this room."

Finney wondered if they had his book. He had mentioned it during his first full-blown interview when McCormack and a film crew came to Norfolk to see how well the judge performed on camera.

The centerpiece of the resort was a large stone-and-masonry building with a Spanish-tile roof and two impressive archways on the front porch. The interior smelled like freshly cut lumber and varnish. Finney guessed that, a few weeks ago, the building might have been some kind of chapel. For the next two weeks, it would serve as the Paradise Courthouse.

"Dinner will be waiting for each of you in your condos," instructed Murphy. "Our camera crews will, of course, be following you, so feel free to engage in any type of religious ceremonies that might be appropriate before or after you eat. We will need you back at the courthouse in two hours." He reached into his backpack and returned everyone's watch.

"We have reset your watches so that we're all on Paradise Island time," he explained. "You need to be back here at 9:00 p.m. sharp. Tammy will be explaining the rules, and you will be getting your first assignment on camera. So dress appropriately."

On the way to his condo, Finney fell in step beside Dr. Kline. She looked like she was born for island life—her sunglasses smacked of island cool, and she had piled her blond hair on top of her head, exposing her perfectly tanned neck. Finney, on the other hand, was already sweating. "Where do you think we are, Doctor?" he asked, not loud enough for the others to hear.

"I don't know. We were blindfolded, remember?"

Two weeks of this, thought Finney. "Yeah, but you must have a guess. I'll tell you what." Finney made a show of glancing around. They were a few steps ahead of the others. Dr. Kline hadn't seemed to notice that Ando had a hard time keeping up. The cameramen were carrying their cameras at their sides. "You tell me what *you* think, and I'll give you *my* guess."

Dr. Kline sighed. "All right. Based on the white sand beaches, palm trees, sea grape trees, cacti, agave, and coral reefs as well as the direction of the trade winds, the range for a Gulfstream IV with a full fuel tank, and the oleanders and royal poincianas growing along this path—I'd say we're somewhere in the eastern South Pacific. Probably near the Galápagos chain."

The Galápagos. Charles Darwin. Evolution. Just the kind of melodramatic location the producers might choose.

Just then an iguana darted across their path, startling Finney. "Not to mention the iguanas," said Dr. Kline. "Native to that band of islands as well."

They walked on a few steps in silence. What Dr. Kline said made sense, except for the style of the architecture. Somehow it seemed out of character for a Pacific island.

"And your guess, Judge Finney?"

"I was going to say we were on an island too," said Finney. It was important to keep the poor country lawyer routine going as long as possible. "Somewhere in the middle of an ocean—most probably the Atlantic or Pacific." He glanced at Kline out of the corner of his eye. It was possible that somewhere under those large-framed sunglasses the pretty eyes were smiling, but he doubted it. "But I'll tell you one thing: it's way too hot for paradise."

CHAPTER 12

They gathered back at Paradise Courthouse a few minutes before nine. Finney had stuffed two suits and one sports coat with matching slacks in his suitcase. For his first court appearance, he wore a two-button suit coat with a blue windowpane pattern and pleated pants that Nikki had begged him to leave in Norfolk. "You'll lose everybody under thirty with those pants," said Nikki. But based on what he'd seen so far of the other contestants, the under-thirty crowd was going to be hard to win no matter what.

The inside of the courthouse could have been transplanted from Norfolk, or just about any other jurisdiction in the Commonwealth of Virginia, except that the hardwood floors had been recently varnished and showed no signs of wear. The harsh television lights bounced off the flat surfaces of the judge's dais, the counsel tables, and the floor, creating a kind of antiseptic glare that Finney found disconcerting. Still, it was a courtroom and it therefore felt like home.

Finney had been assigned to sit at the table on the right side of the courtroom, next to the ever-serious Kareem Hasaan. *A bad spot,* thought Finney, since Hasaan had him beat in both the physique and clothing departments. The Arab's suit screamed money, a dark-gray pinstriped three-button model with a matching pocket square and wide lapels. A monogrammed shirt, cuff links, the works. No pleats on this guy, of course. Finney leaned away from his tablemate—no sense making it easy for the cameramen to get them both in the same shot.

The other three contestants shared the opposite counsel table—a real mishmash of styles. The Swami opted for casual chic, with a wrinkled sports coat and open-collar shirt. Dr. Ando apparently decided to dress the part of a Buddhist monk, his one-size-fits-all robe swallowing his pint-sized body. And then there was the stunning Dr. Kline.

Finney stole a few sideways glances at Kline, not the way a younger man might look, not the way he noticed the Swami stealing glances, but the way a lawyer sizes up opposing counsel before a case, wondering how much the natural beauty will convert to jury appeal. Kline had large blue eyes, accentuated by dark eye shadow, and a slender nose. She had a broad mouth and pouty lips, and she wore her blond hair pulled back in a tight ponytail. Even when she was in a skirt suit, you could tell that Victoria didn't miss many days at the gym—there was no hiding the definition in those calf muscles.

Finney thought about the young men watching the show. Maybe he should have brought Nikki Moreno to argue for Christianity. Except, of course, that she wasn't a Christian yet. But the judge was working on it. Another reason, he reminded himself, for doing this program. Nikki had promised to rally support and handle PR for the judge's cause. For Christ's cause. To do so, she would have to watch every minute of every show.

It would help Finney define his style. He'd be speaking to a lot of folks just like Nikki, so he would pretend that she was his only audience. Every speech he made, every question he asked, every answer he gave would be articulated with Nikki Moreno in mind. If he could convince Nikki, he would probably end up reaching thousands of others as well.

Before they started rolling, McCormack filled them in on a few logistics. They would be on Paradise Island for two weeks. A week from Friday, everybody would be sent home except the two finalists, who would be asked to stay for an additional day. The method of choosing the finalists would be revealed later.

As with other innovative reality shows, the network was running a pilot during the summer months to see what kind of ratings the show would generate. If it did well, a sequel would follow next year.

Throughout the month of June, the show would air twice a week—

Tuesdays and Thursdays. After those eight episodes, they would skip Tuesday, July 4, and the final episode would be aired on Thursday, July 6. They would be filming something most every day, and editing would be tight. Most reality shows were recorded weeks or even months before they aired. But not this one. They had considered doing the whole thing live, but it would have cost too much to keep everybody on the island for five straight weeks. So they would be doing the next best thing. The first two weeks of the show would air while the contestants were still on the island. The last three weeks would air immediately afterward. McCormack reminded everyone that they had signed a confidentiality agreement promising they wouldn't divulge any aspects of the filming or results until after the final episode aired.

It would not be unusual for segments shot one day to be edited and aired the next. The contestants should treat this like live television, because that's essentially what it was. In fact, if the contestants messed up royally, they could be pretty certain that their mistakes would be featured in the next show, since that kind of thing makes for good television. Even Finney's stomach got a little riled by that comment—the prospect of the entire nation watching his biggest faux pas.

Without asking for questions, McCormack stepped aside and started counting down the seconds. Tammy toed her spot at the front of the courtroom, looking glamorous but stiff as she addressed the contestants.

"Each of you has been chosen to represent one of the prominent faith groups in America," she said on cue. "You've been selected because you have a rare combination of theological and legal training and because you are passionate advocates for your faith. In addition, your various life experiences demonstrate that your faith can help you survive the worst of times."

Tammy paused and turned woodenly, looking into a different camera that apparently represented the viewing audience. "Each of those traits will be put to the test in the upcoming weeks as these advocates defend their faith in this courtroom and try to live their faith on Paradise Island.

We will put the advocates through a literal hell on earth because we know that Americans are not just looking for a faith that makes sense but also a faith that survives when everything else is falling apart.

"The rules are simple. Each week you will see the contestants advocate for their faith in this courtroom. And in each episode, you will see the advocates confront the issues that an authentic faith helps us address—temptation, injustice, trauma, sickness, shame, forgiveness, and love."

Tammy turned to face the contestants again as Finney wondered what the producers had up their sleeves that could address all of those issues. His mind flashed back to the release he had signed—maybe he should have read it with more care.

"This show will use an innovative combination of two types of verdicts. The first verdict will be delivered by a judge here on Paradise Island—a certified agnostic whom you will meet in a few minutes. That verdict will be revealed immediately following the courtroom activity for that week. Our viewers will learn of this verdict when the show airs on Tuesday nights. A second verdict—a *jury* verdict—will be rendered by the viewers themselves. Our viewers will vote by phone following the airing of the Tuesday night show for a period of four hours. Their jury verdict will be announced on the Thursday-night show.

"For each judge and jury verdict you receive, *Faith on Trial* will make a donation of fifty thousand dollars to a charity of your choice. In addition, two finalists will be chosen to compete on the very last show through a method that will be revealed later. The overall winner will be awarded one million dollars for his or her favorite charity."

Finney could hardly imagine a better scenario. Even if he performed miserably and never obtained a verdict from the agnostic judge, he was pretty sure that the Christian viewers, who would far outnumber the viewers from the other faith groups, would grant him a jury verdict nearly every show. But just as he was thinking about his charity of choice, Tammy turned to another camera and flashed a nervous smile.

"There is, of course, a twist," she said. "We want to see how persuasive our contestants are, not just gauge the number of viewers watching from any given faith group. Therefore, we've conducted an independent poll of television viewers who said they were planning on watching the show." While Tammy was talking, a large flat-screen monitor automatically lowered from the ceiling behind the judge's bench, and a chart appeared on the screen.

"Judge Finney, we found that seventy-four percent of potential viewers labeled themselves as Christians already. Mr. Hasaan, four percent of potential viewers said they were Muslim. Mr. Hadji, one percent are Hindu…"

"Cool," said the Swami.

"One percent Buddhist, Dr. Ando. And Dr. Kline, when we subtract our Jewish viewers, that leaves approximately fifteen percent who are either agnostic or belong to some other religion not already mentioned."

Victoria Kline nodded, looking determined to double that number before the show was over. Finney coughed, but nothing major, just a polite little smoker's hack.

"To win a jury verdict, you must show you are making converts," said Tammy. "Which means that you will be judged based on the percentage of viewers *above* this baseline percentage who are calling to support your cause."

Finney stared at the percentage for Christians as if by sheer willpower he could reduce that huge number to something more reasonable. Seventy-four percent? Either the show's producers had surveyed every Christian in America, or a lot of nominal Christians who hadn't seen the inside of a church in years answered the survey. Or they had rigged the show.

"All rise!" shouted the court clerk. "The Honorable Judge Howard Javitts presiding. All those with pleas to enter and arguments to be heard should now draw near. God save this honorable court." The clerk looked at Dr. Kline and smirked. "Assuming, of course, there is a God."

"You may be seated," said His Honor.

Javitts glared at the contestants as if daring them to challenge his authority. His square face featured wrinkle lines that creased deep into his forehead when he scowled, which was most of the time. His broad and flat nose gave him the appearance of a former heavyweight boxer who now took out his aggression in the courtroom. The man was probably gunning for his own judge show when this stint was over, reasoned Finney.

Javitts lectured the contestants on the rules of decorum, his bass voice filling the courtroom. Javitts had the voice of God, thought Finney, though not His visage. Finney preferred a smiling Jesus, One who enjoyed us too much to be constantly frowning.

Javitts finished his lecture and immediately dished out the first assignment. Court would reconvene tomorrow morning at 9:00 a.m., and each contestant would give an eight-minute opening statement—not a minute more, because the judge himself would be keeping time. Were there any questions?

Hearing none, the judge adjourned court for the day, and the cameras stopped rolling for a moment. "That's a wrap," said McCormack.

Murphy strolled to the front of the courtroom with his hands in his pockets to address the contestants. "Most of you have probably already discovered that we've placed a desktop computer with Internet access in your room. We want you to feel free to use that computer for research, for notes, whatever.

"However, keep in mind that your Internet access will be monitored and, in fact, filtered. Any attempts to access video of the shows already aired, or to access press stories or other information about the shows, or to communicate with anyone outside of Paradise Island about any aspects of the show, will result in your immediate dismissal. The computers are provided for the purpose of doing research about the various faith issues involved in this reality show and for that purpose only. Are there any questions about that?"

Nobody raised a hand, so Murphy continued. "The camera crews will be following you back to your condos and shooting some footage tonight. Plus, as I'm sure you noticed, there are wall-mounted bubble cameras in every room of your condo except the bathroom. Feel free to go through the same types of prayer or meditation ceremonies that you would on any other night. It wouldn't hurt if we caught some of that on camera to use as B-roll."

This, Finney reminded himself, was what he hated most about television. Everything was so phony. *Stage a little prayer time for me,* Murphy was basically saying. Viewers might be fascinated to see the Swami burning incense and performing rituals in front of some small shrine, or Kareem on his prayer rug facing Mecca, but Finney's prayers were much less exotic. Besides, he didn't like the idea of praying for show.

Jesus must have seen a day like this coming. *When you pray, don't be like the hypocrites who pray standing in the temple and on the street corners,* Jesus had warned. *But when you pray, go into your private room, close your door, and pray to your Father in secret.*

The problem on Paradise Island was the lack of a private room. There was no place to pray secretly except… Wait! There was one place where the cameras wouldn't follow him. A bathroom is not exactly the first thing that springs to mind when you think of a prayer closet, but then again, privacy is privacy.

CHAPTER 13

What do you think about Skyler Hadji?" Bryce McCormack asked. He took a swig from his iced tea and eyed the beer in Murphy's hand. There was a price to pay for being an obsessive perfectionist as a reality-show director. Part of it was not drinking on nights during the shoot.

"Are you kidding?" replied Murphy. "He's perfect. Makes me want to convert to Hinduism." He took another pull on his beer and set it down on the patio next to his cushioned lounge chair. "Assuming they can drink."

"They say his condo already looks like a Hindu temple—idols every-where, incense, the whole works," Bryce said.

Murphy didn't respond.

"What about Finney?" Bryce asked.

A pause as both men studied the night. "Reminds me of my old man," Murphy confessed, looking out at the ocean. The offhand comment sur-prised Bryce. There were a few things the two men didn't talk about, an unwritten rule. Murphy's domineering father was his forbidden subject; for Bryce, it was a daughter's suicide.

But there was something about the island breeze and the Jimmy Buf-fett music that caused a man to let his guard down. Bryce could feel it too, and he was stone-cold sober.

"You think he's that bad?" Bryce asked.

Murphy considered this for a moment. "Nobody's that bad. Plus, Finney's too cagey to come across looking anything like my old man. But he's got a lot of the same characteristics."

"And never got along with his own son," Bryce added, knowing this was going through Murphy's mind as well.

"Imagine that."

Bryce let the silence hang for a few minutes. He had met Murphy five years ago, long after the man had changed his first name, last name, drug habits (mostly), and occupation. They started doing reality shows together, and the two developed a solid friendship. He knew enough about Cameron Murphy's father not to push the issue. Bryce's own father had been proud of his son's brief Hollywood success and even the reality shows Bryce now found himself directing. But Pastor Ronald Martin had not merely withheld approval; he'd actually led a boycott against his son's most recent reality-show offering. It didn't help when *Marriage Under Fire* got dumped after its first season.

"What's New York think about the buzz?" McCormack asked, sensing they needed a change in subject.

It was dark, but he could hear the smile in Murphy's voice. "This thing is hot, Bryce. The Anti-Defamation League is fired up, screaming loudly. After our teasers, the right-wing fundamentalists are thinking about joining them."

My teasers, Bryce thought. Murphy was the producer, but Bryce and a screenwriter friend had brainstormed the concepts for the spots. *Temptation, trials, and faith.* One of the teasers featured Tammy in the smallest of bikinis, which promised to test the resolve of the male contestants to keep the faith. The spots made *Desperate Housewives* promos look like teasers for *Father Knows Best.*

Murphy burped, his way of rubbing in the fact that he was enjoying a beer while Bryce played the prude. The thing that drove Bryce nuts was that *he* ended up with the beer gut while Murphy's incredible metabolism burned away every ounce of fat on his body.

"Christians are so predictable," Murphy said. "They're saying it doesn't treat faith with the proper respect. Another example of the Hollywood crowd being out of touch. All that crap. Our network execs pulled the ads right on schedule, promising a show respectful of our valued religious diversity. Or some nonsense like that."

The whirlwinds of controversy, Bryce thought, *blowing money right out of the trees.* You couldn't buy this kind of publicity. They were fast becoming *The Passion* of the reality-show genre. Or perhaps *The Da Vinci Code* was a more apt analogy—something the Religious Right could denounce while they all read it.

"I even sent my old man an anonymous letter with a copy of the promo tape for the show," Murphy said. "He'll probably be leading the charge."

Bryce smiled at the thought but also grasped the underlying desperation that it signaled. "Murph, this show's gonna work," Bryce said. "And if it doesn't, we'll bounce back. We always do."

"No," Murphy said, barely loud enough to be heard above Jimmy Buffett. "There's no second chance this time. This one's *got* to work."

McCormack sighed and finished his iced tea. Murphy was a talented producer but one who had lost the fun of the business a long time ago. Ratings and reputation meant everything to Murphy. Lately, he hadn't had much of either.

And even for Bryce, his one cult-following hit on the big screen seemed like a lifetime ago. These days, he scrounged around with Murphy on the scrap pile of reality TV. What did that one guy call it? "The vast wasteland of television" or something like that.

There was another thing Bryce needed to get on the table, and this might be his last chance to bring it up. "Murph," Bryce said softly, "we don't need any miracles here. We've got enough juice without manufacturing anything."

He sensed Murphy stiffen. "We've been through this," Murphy replied.

"It's not right, Murph. I mean it's your call. But if it were up to me, I'd play the Muslim guy straight up. And I'm not one to shy away from

risks." Bryce knew the show would receive intensive scrutiny. Why set up
a fake healing and risk getting caught?

"Hasaan needs our help," Murphy replied. He shifted in his lounger,
sitting forward. "We're just leveling the playing field a little. Americans
prejudge all Muslims these days. You know it's true, Bryce, and that's why
you chose Kareem in the first place—fits the stereotype perfectly. Even
though he didn't meet the sickness criteria."

Bryce didn't bother responding. He'd learned that often the best way
to argue with Murphy was to bite his tongue. When Murphy realized he
could get his way, he would start feeling bad about pushing too far. Before
long, Murphy would start back-pedaling on his own.

But not tonight. "He's your guy, Bryce. *You* talked *me* into putting
him on the show," Murphy continued. "I never liked the idea of the
staged medical tests in the first place. Sooner or later, our boy finds out
that he's fine, and then we're toast. I'm just saying, let's preempt all those
problems by discovering right on the show that he's been healed." Murphy paused, perhaps to see how well this was being received. "The show
giveth and the show taketh away. Blessed be the name of the show."

Murphy lifted his beer in a solitary toast to his own wittiness, then
drained it. He set down the empty and burped loudly, as if he were a judge
banging his gavel to seal off further debate. Case closed.

Further argument tonight, Bryce knew, would only cause Murphy to
dig in deeper. Instead, Bryce would come back to it later from a different
angle.

His apparent acquiescence allowed the tension to seep out of the air
as Jimmy Buffett gave way to Kenny Chesney. The two friends soaked up
the night in silence, each lost in his own thoughts.

"Well," said Murphy a few minutes later, "better head back to my
place. Big day tomorrow."

"Yeah," said Bryce.

They walked into the condo, and Murphy threw his empty bottle in the trash. "Any predictions?" he asked on the way out.

"Name calling, controversy, boycotts, and high ratings," McCormack replied.

"No. I mean about who's going to win."

"You know who my favorite is," said Bryce.

Murphy turned and looked at him. "Not a chance," scoffed Murphy. And they both knew he wasn't talking about the show. "She's way out of your league."

"What about you?" asked Bryce.

Murphy shrugged his shoulders, turning to leave. "Anybody but Finney."

∾

Finney snuffed out his cigar, jotted a few more notes on his yellow legal pad, and looked up a verse of Scripture. He glanced up at the camera on the wall again, feeling conspicuous, ever mindful of the fact that he was being watched. He thought about how boring this would be for the person who had to review the tapes. Finney had watched a few other reality shows, and the characters were always doing something interesting, usually hooking up with a member of the opposite sex. But here he sat. Smoking cigars and reading his Bible.

This experience was a lot different from what Finney had thought it would be. He wasn't sure what he had expected; he just knew it wasn't *this*. The other contestants were all so much younger, except for Dr. Ando. Only Kareem and Finney appeared to have much courtroom experience. But Finney sensed that courtroom tactics would be a small part of what it would take to win this contest, though he didn't have the foggiest idea what else might be required.

For some reason, meeting the other contestants had made him less focused on winning. Yes, he still wanted to represent his faith well. But he didn't want to embarrass or humiliate the others on national television. Before today, the show was just a fascinating intellectual challenge, one that Finney thought could dramatically advance the Christian message. But now real people were attached to these other faiths. People who, for the most part, Finney already liked.

He put his Bible down and stood up to face the wide-angle bubble camera mounted on the wall. He scratched the back of his neck and frowned. No wonder he had never tried acting. He cleared his throat and got a little cough out of the way before proceeding.

"This is not going to be easy," he told the camera. "But I'm not going to attack the advocates for the other faith groups. I'm committed to the truth, so I'll have to point out where their beliefs are wrong, but I'm going to keep the focus on Jesus and try to act like He would if He were in my shoes. And I don't really think it serves any useful purpose to attack their faith as opposed to showing them why they should believe in mine."

He hesitated for a moment, though he was not sure why. It wasn't as if the camera was going to respond. "Well, that's about it. I'm going to pray and then try to get a little rest."

Finney returned to his chair, took off his John Deere cap, and placed his elbows on his knees, bowing his head. All he could think about was that blasted camera filming the top of his mostly bald head.

After a few minutes, he stood and decided to address the camera one more time. "God hears me whether I pray out loud or silently," Finney lectured. "It's not like I've got to slit my wrists and yell real loud to get His attention."

Not long afterward, Finney turned off the lights and crawled into bed. He was dog-tired but knew he would have a hard time falling asleep with the bedroom camera focused on him, its red light reminding Finney that the entire nation might enjoy watching him snore. He rolled over so that his back was to the camera and began to pray in earnest. Before long, he had forgotten about the one-eyed monster. The bravado was gone now too. Finney had learned a long time ago that false fronts don't work well with God.

"Please don't let me embarrass Your name tomorrow," he prayed.

CHAPTER 14

L adies and gentlemen of the jury," Finney began. He thought it was clever that the show's producers had asked the set extras to sit in the jury box along with some employees of the Paradise Island resort. It gave him somebody to focus on, somebody to think about other than the four contestants shooting daggers at him from their counsel tables.

Finney had drawn the short straw. Somebody had to go first.

"I could talk to you today about the contrasting philosophies of the various religions. Or I could explain the historic tenets and doctrines of the Christian faith. Or argue about ways that Christianity has made the world better. But this occasion is too important and my time is too short to spend it that way."

Finney leaned forward on the podium that separated him from the jury. Judge Javitts had said the advocates could pace the courtroom if they liked, but Finney believed in protocol. If the jury wanted flamboyant, they would be hearing from the Swami soon enough.

"Instead, I want to talk to you about a man named Jesus. Because to accept Him is to accept the Christian faith, and to reject Him is to reject the Christian faith. And because He is, with all due respect to the other religions represented here today, the single-most-important figure in world history."

Out of the corner of his eye, Finney could see Kareem bristle, but he couldn't worry about hurt feelings. Eight minutes was not a lot of time.

"Nobody taught like Jesus," Finney said. And he waited a few seconds for that to sink in. "Two thousand years ago, in a chauvinistic and intolerant society, Jesus broke down longstanding barriers based on sex, nationality, and occupation. His followers included a tax collector and a former harlot. He ministered to the 'untouchables' of His day, those with leprosy. A few years after His death, the leading advocate for the early church, a man named Paul, summed it up this way: 'There is no Jew or Greek, slave or free, male or female; for you are all one in Christ Jesus.'

"But that's not all. In a society characterized by 'might makes right,' at a time when His own people expected Him to lead a military revolt against the Roman Empire, Jesus taught His disciples to turn the other cheek. He told them to love their enemies and pray for those who persecuted them. He told them that great leaders must first be humble servants. And He washed the feet of His disciples."

Finney turned and walked to the counsel table where Skyler Hadji sat between Drs. Ando and Kline. He gestured toward Hadji, the only one who seemed to be enjoying the judge's performance. "Even one of this man's icons, Mahatma Gandhi, recognized the inspired nature of Jesus's teaching. 'It is the Sermon on the Mount that endeared Jesus to me,' Gandhi once said. And on another occasion, speaking about the Christian religion, he said, 'I like their Christ; I don't like their Christians.'

"And many times, Mr. Hadji, I have to agree with him." Finney thought he noticed a slight nod from Hadji. Could it be this easy?

Emboldened, the judge made a sweeping gesture toward the others. "What man or woman here would say that Jesus was not an inspired teacher, an enlightened prophet, light-years ahead of His time both morally and ethically?" Finney waited in silence, each second driving home his point, until finally he turned back to the jury.

And then it hit. The worst timing possible. He reached for the glass on his counsel table and took a quick drink of water, but nothing could stop it. Finney had been finding it increasingly hard to catch his breath during these coughing spells, and today was no exception. He coughed and hacked for a moment, his face flushing with the effort, until at last he regained his composure and smiled at the jury.

"Sometimes I even choke myself up," he said, but only one or two even gave him a token smile. How many times had he told lawyers that the courtroom was no place for humor?

"Where was I? Oh yeah—nobody taught like Jesus. Nobody lived like Him, either. Jesus was a prophet who backed up His teaching with His life. But there's more to Him than that. Because nobody died like Him."

Finney settled in behind the podium again as he talked about the suffering and death of Jesus. He briefly explained the horrible Roman practice of crucifixion and the reason that Jesus willingly took His place on the cross.

"What other founder of a world religion died so that His followers might live? Others died in a state of meditation or from an unexpected sickness, but who else allowed Himself to be nailed to a tree so that His followers might find favor with God?"

"Four minutes, Mr. Finney," said the voice of God from the judge's bench.

That guy needs to go to judge school—learn a little courtroom decorum.

"Yes, Your Honor," said Finney.

"And nobody rose like Jesus," Finney continued, gathering steam as he approached his final point. This would be his strength—his specialty, if he had one. Finney had always believed that the one thing that distinguished Christianity was the ironclad proof of the Resurrection. He had devoted a whole chapter to it in *The Cross Examination of Jesus Christ.* "It all rises or falls with the third day," Finney sometimes said, though he knew better than to use anything that hokey in this setting.

He mentioned a few factors supporting the reliability of the gospel witnesses—the archaeology that confirmed the gospel accounts and the twenty-four thousand ancient manuscripts, including more than five thousand five hundred Greek manuscripts, that contained and verified various portions of the New Testament records. Plus, Finney said, the gospel accounts have the "ring of truth—the ragged edges that reflect the way things happen in real life."

"Why else, at a time when women were prohibited from testifying in a court of law, would the gospel writers say women first discovered the empty tomb? Why else would they paint the disciples as scared and skeptical followers of Christ—men who returned to their jobs after Christ died, not believing that He would actually come back from the dead?"

Finney's questions started flowing faster as he noticed the judge glance down at his watch. "Did you know that for more than sixteen hundred years nobody even suggested the tomb was not empty? How could the early church have started in Jerusalem, just a stone's throw from the tomb, if Christ's body were lying in the grave? Peter's powerful sermon on the day of Pentecost, when three thousand souls were saved in one day, would have been categorically refuted by the decaying body of Jesus Christ in a nearby tomb."

Finney stopped and caught his breath, moved out from behind the podium, and lowered his tone. "Those who contest His resurrection today tend to gravitate toward one of two theories. Some say the whole Resurrection thing is a legend, cooked up by the church years after the life of Christ. Others say it is a conspiracy or fraud, cobbled together by the disciples so they could take their place at the head of a major world religion.

"The legend theory is easy to refute. Some distinguished scholars have spent their entire lives studying things like the length of time that it takes for a legend to develop. According to their research, it takes a minimum of two generations, *with no written documentation in existence,* for a legend to develop that will supersede the actual facts.

"Think about it in a context we can more readily understand. Let's say I've never argued a case in front of the Supreme Court. If somebody wanted to create a legend about me, saying I won twenty straight cases there, would they be able to do it within thirty years of my death, at a time when thousands of people who knew me were still alive?

"The first gospel account was written within thirty years of the life of Christ. When that account was written, many witnesses to the death and resurrection of Jesus were still living. According to the experts, there is no example of a legendary tale in ancient history that developed in so short a period of time. None. Ever."

"Two minutes."

Finney shot the judge an annoyed look before turning back to the jury. "And this theory that it was just a conspiracy by the disciples…" Finney shook his head, hoping the jury was with him. "I've tried enough cases to see every kind of conspiracy imaginable. I've seen men and women lie to make money, to further their own reputations, to gain political power, or to save their own skins. But I've never seen men and women lie so they could be tortured and burned at the stake. I've never seen them conspire so they could be crucified like their leader. Death has a way of revealing truth. Why would the disciples die for a lie?"

Finney surveyed the jury and noticed a woman in the back row fighting to keep her eyes open. How could she sleep through *this?* He was discussing the most significant event in the history of the planet. He wanted to throw something at her.

He decided against it.

"Imagine for a moment that you are the apostle Peter. You've either seen a resurrected Jesus or you're making it all up—one big practical joke on all mankind. You are hauled before the Jewish rulers—the Sanhedrin—and ordered not to talk about Jesus and the Resurrection. But you keep preaching. You see your friends stoned, whipped, and jailed for the faith. But you keep preaching. Emperor Nero of Rome declares himself the 'enemy of God,' and you see Christians tied to posts, covered in wax, and set ablaze to light the Roman roads at night. But you go out and convert others to take their places, telling everyone you see about the Resurrection.

"You are arrested and thrown in the Mamertine prison in Rome—a death cell where you are chained upright to a post and made to stand in your own urine and excrement for nine long months. Your only exposure to light comes when the guards haul you out of prison to torture you.

Renounce Christ and you will go free. But you refuse to become a traitor to your faith.

"Finally you are hauled before Nero to face execution. There you see your beloved wife, whom you have not seen since the day of your arrest nine months ago. If you renounce the Resurrection now, she will be spared. And you will be released."

Finney paused and studied the jury. They were all with him, all except one...and as long as she didn't snore.

"But you hold firm and Nero announces your penalty—crucifixion for you and your wife. Do you renounce now, at the last possible moment?

"No!" Finney slapped the jury rail, and the lady in the back snapped to attention, a possible whiplash victim. "Your resolve strengthens. You insist on being crucified upside down because you are not worthy to die like your Savior. And as you are being led away, you look over your shoulder and make eye contact with your trembling wife. 'Oh thou,' you say, 'remember the Lord.'

"Can anyone seriously believe that Peter did this for a hoax? for a conspiracy? Or had he seen the resurrected Christ with his own eyes and felt Christ's power in every sinew of his body?

"Peter didn't ask to be crucified upside down because he was a ringleader in some plot to deceive. He asked because he had heard Christ teach and he had watched Christ die and then he had seen Christ come back from the dead. It was the most important event in history, with the most important Man who ever lived at the center of it.

"And Peter had seen it all with his own eyes."

"Your time is up, Judge Finney."

"Thank you, Your Honor," said Finney. He felt almost breathless, but he was satisfied that he had given it his best shot. He turned to sit back down.

"Not so fast," said the big, booming voice.

Huh?

"I do have two quick questions for you."

Finney faced the judge. "Okay."

Javitts looked down at his notes. "In your understanding, is it ever permissible for a Christian to kill another human being?"

Finney thought about this for a long moment. *Where did that come from?*

"Mr. Finney?"

"Sorry, Your Honor. Jesus said to love your enemies, not to seek revenge. So I would say an individual should never take the life of another except in self-defense. But sometimes the state must do so through its citizens, including Christian citizens, in order to punish wrongdoers or defend its national interests."

Judge Javitts showed no reaction. "Okay, then, let me ask you this: Is it ever permissible for a Christian to take his or her own life?"

The judge had his pen poised over his legal pad, as if it was the most natural thing in the world to ask these questions and take a few notes. But Finney hadn't said a thing about suicide during his entire opening statement. *Where are these questions coming from?*

"No, Your Honor. Most Christians believe that doing so would usurp the prerogative of God. And we also believe that life is always worth living—that God gives grace sufficient for even the most drastic circumstances. Committing suicide is wrong, but it doesn't somehow negate a person's faith. A Christian who commits suicide is still a Christian."

"I see," said Javitts. "Thank you, Judge Finney."

Chapter 15

adji was next. What he lacked in courtroom experience he more than made up for with enthusiasm. "Man, that dude is smart," he said, shaking his head and embarrassing Judge Finney. "How do you follow an act like that?"

He shoved his hands into the pockets of his jeans. If he had been a lawyer in Finney's court, he would have spent the night in jail for wearing jeans and a blue blazer to court, but this was TV.

"I've got no problem with the Resurrection," he said casually.

The admission floored Finney. He scribbled a note, hoping the jury was paying attention.

"I mean, I wasn't there and neither was Judge O, so we'll probably never know, but a truly advanced yogi could do something like that."

Finney blinked. The Swami had a way of just conversationally saying mind-blowing stuff, and the jury looked like they were swallowing every word of it. "In fact," he continued, "some Hindus believe that Christianity is just modified Hinduism and that Jesus lived in India between the ages of thirteen and thirty-one."

The Swami shrugged. "I don't know about all that. But let me tell you a few things I do know about."

For the next several minutes, the Swami painted an appealing picture of Hinduism, explaining the concept of Brahmin, the supreme god, the ultimate reality, the world soul. He talked about karma, and Finney had to admit that this kid had more than his share of good karma. And then, in his ever-so-casual way, the Swami moved on to the issue of samsara.

"Did you ever wonder why bad things happen to good people—or why good things happen to bad people, for that matter?"

A few of the jurors actually nodded.

"Did you ever think that you must be missing something? Well, turns out you are.

"You're just looking at one snapshot in time," said the Swami, "and so life sometimes seems unfair. But all souls experience samsara, or transmigration, a long-lasting cycle of births and rebirths. When you look at someone and judge what's happening to them based only on this life, you're missing a big part of the motion picture of their soul's migration."

The jurors looked a little confused, and the Swami must have noticed it. "If that's hard for you to understand, it's okay. You'll figure it out in your next life."

It did Finney good to see the Swami's jokes bomb too. And Letterman thought he had tough crowds.

"Have you ever experienced a sense of déjà vu? I've been here before. I've done this before. But you know for certain that this is the first time it's happened in *this* life. Where do you think that sense of déjà vu comes from?"

Next to Finney, Kareem was grunting his disapproval. "Are we having fun yet?" asked Finney.

"You smell like smoke," said Kareem.

The Swami decided it was time for show and tell. He walked behind his counsel table and emerged with a small carved image. To Finney, it looked like an Asian monk, sitting yoga style, with multiple arms and multiple heads.

The Swami placed the idol on the rail of the witness stand. "People say that Hindus worship hundreds of gods, thousands even. Gods like this one—Vishnu."

Kareem shot to his feet. "I object, Your Honor." Finney didn't even know you *could* object. What were the rules for game-show trials?

"On what grounds?" asked Javitts.

"Idol worship," insisted Kareem, as if the rules for trials prohibited such a thing. "There is no god but Allah. This man"—he pointed an accusatory finger at Hadji—"should not be allowed to subject the rest of us to the worship of one of his thousands of gods."

"Overruled," said Javitts. "You'll have your turn."

Kareem didn't try to hide his displeasure.

Hadji turned to face his adversary. If Kareem was trying to throw Hadji off stride with his objection, it didn't appear to be working. "It's not idol worship when I just place Vishnu on this rail," explained Hadji calmly. "I'll let you know when we start the actual worship." Kareem glared at the man. "And we don't actually believe in thousands of *gods*, Mr. Hasaan. There is only one transcendent force—Brahmin—but this supreme being manifests himself in an infinite number of ways. Think of it as a billion snapshots of one supreme god rather than a billion different gods."

Hadji then walked to his counsel table, ignoring the simmering Kareem. He paused for a drink of water.

"Four minutes," said Javitts.

"I cannot drink this water directly; I need a vessel to help lift it to my lips. So it is with Brahmin and our idols. The mind sometimes needs a tangible thing to help direct our adoration of an intangible supreme being. Other religions do the same thing, with a cross or a temple or a prayer rug."

"Objection!" shouted Kareem, on his feet again. "Now this man accuses *me* of idol worship!"

"Mr. Hasaan, sit down!" Javitts ordered.

Kareem remained standing.

"Mr. Hasaan."

"Your Honor, it is one thing to argue for your religion. It is quite another to do so by denigrating and mischaracterizing the religions of others. With all due respect, if the court's not going to say something about it, then I must."

Finney watched the lines on Javitts's face tighten. This was a direct challenge to the court's authority, and all the alpha males in the courtroom knew it. Finney had dealt with this type of thing himself many times as a judge. Some litigants, like Kareem, turned every minor skirmish into World War III. It really came down to this: who will run the courtroom— the judge or the lawyers?

"Overruled, Mr. Hasaan. *Sit...down!*"

When Kareem still didn't move, Finney knew that the man's anger was just a strategy. The issue that had caused the objection was merely an excuse for an early showdown. Hadji's case had been effectively interrupted, and the Muslim had made *his* point—if you mess with the advocate for Muhammad, you'd better be ready for a fight.

"You're risking contempt," Javitts warned.

"I don't recall a prison on the Paradise Island tour," Kareem said. Finney saw a flash of panic from a judge whose bluff had been exposed. Then Javitts's face flushed in anger, and Kareem, totally in control, slowly pulled out his chair and took his seat.

Round one, Finney thought, *for Kareem.*

∾

Once Kareem had made his point, Hadji completed his opening without further incident. Afterward, Kareem delivered his own thunderous opening, extolling the merits of Islam while being careful not to malign the other religions. When he concluded, Judge Javitts posed the same two questions he had asked Finney and Hadji.

"In your faith, is it permissible for a Muslim to kill another human being, Mr. Hasaan?"

Kareem smiled thinly, then scowled. "That is, of course, the question Americans have been asking me since 9/11. What is a jihad? Do Muslims believe that the hijackers were justified?"

Kareem zeroed in on Javitts, his face taut. "I condemn those actions in no uncertain terms, as do all true Muslims. Ours is a peaceful religion. The 9/11 terrorists hijacked our religion as surely as they did those airplanes. Nothing in the teachings of Muhammad legitimizes the killing of civilians."

Kareem took a deep breath and continued. "But with that said, the answer to your question is an emphatic yes—killing for the right cause can be just. Do you need me to cite the Koran verses? 'Fight those who do not believe in Allah, nor in the latter day.' That's Sura 9:29. Or how about, 'Surely Allah loves those who fight in His way in ranks as if they were a firm and compact wall'? That's Sura 61:4.

"And then there are the promises that Allah will grant special favors for those who die in a holy war. We do not shirk from these teachings, Judge Javitts."

Kareem let the silence linger to emphasize his point. He presented an imposing figure as he stood there unblinking in front of the judge.

"But to judge my religion on the basis of the hijackers is to judge Christianity on the basis of David Koresh or the Ku Klux Klan.

"Do not the other religions represented here talk about 'just wars' as well? Judge Finney cleverly disguised the issue, saying that Christians are not allowed to kill as individuals but may be called on as part of an army to defend national security. That is nothing more than a polite way of saying that people of Judge Finney's religion are killing people of my religion every single day. And they're doing so for political reasons and to protect oil reserves—all in the name of justice."

Kareem motioned to the other counsel table. "And then, of course, there is Dr. Ando's religion, considered by many to be a religion of peace. Did not the Zen priests during World War II train the Japanese kamikaze pilots? Did they not tell them that they would gain improved karma for the next life by their suicide missions?"

He turned back to Javitts. "We all have our suicide bombers, Your

Honor. But that doesn't change the fact that Islam is a religion of peace that only justifies killing in the context of a just and holy war and never justifies the intentional killing of civilians."

"What about suicide?" asked Javitts. "Is it ever permissible for a Muslim to take his or her own life?"

"Only in the context of sacrificing one's own life to save the lives of others or to advance the cause of Allah. In times of war, we call that heroism."

"Thank you, Mr. Hasaan."

∽

Kareem's argument was followed by a smooth presentation from Dr. Kline. After another break, so that the production crew could discuss camera angles and lighting, Judge Javitts gaveled the proceedings to order and called the name of Dr. Hokoji Ando.

The Buddhist advocate rose slowly and limped to the jury box. He stood there stiffly in front of them, his hands folded together. "Pardon my slowness," he said, "but I have fibrodysplasia ossificans progressiva, commonly referred to as FOP. It is a rare and incurable disease that causes bone to form in my muscles, in my tendons, and in my ligaments. There is nothing the doctors can do except monitor the spread of the disease. My body is literally forming a second skeleton, a bone-shaped prison of its own making."

Ando spoke so softly that Finney had to lean forward to hear him. It occurred to Finney that everybody had stopped fidgeting, taking a cue from the unmoving advocate in front of them.

"The average life span of a person with FOP is forty-five years. I have cheated that number by nearly two decades. People with this disease literally turn into living statues—their bodies welded into position like a plastic doll. We suffocate because the bone growth restricts our breathing, literally strangling us."

He paused, letting the full weight of his condition sink in. Finney noticed no sadness in the man's eyes, just a stoic resignation to his lot in life. "What explains this?" Ando asked. "Is it the Christian God of love who saddled me with this condition even before I was born? Or was it Allah, the god of perfect justice, who decided to punish me before I even drew my first breath?"

"Objection!"

Finney couldn't believe that Kareem had the audacity to object at this moment. Didn't he understand anything about sympathy? Didn't he know anything about the subtleties of trying a case? Staking out your turf early was one thing, but this was just plain stupid.

"Overruled," said Javitts without even glancing in Kareem's direction.

Finney leaned over to Kareem. "You're not helping yourself with all these objections," he whispered.

"You try your case; I'll try mine."

And look like a jerk in the process, Finney thought.

"Does science explain it?" continued Ando. "Am I just another mutation in the endless march of the human race to evolve into a higher form? Look at me—am I a higher form? Are two skeletons better than one?"

He stared evenly at the jury, oblivious to the other contestants, the words falling softly from his lips like the hiss of incoming missiles.

"Who explains this? Only Buddha explains this. Only Buddha makes sense of a world steeped in suffering.

"'Life is suffering,' Buddha said. 'Suffering is caused by our attachments to the world. We can end suffering by developing nonattachment and following the Eightfold Path.'

"What is the body, really? What more is it than a skin bag filled with bones, flesh, muscle, organs, and fluid? Free yourself from the body. Settle the mind. I will show you how even an old man with FOP can find enlightenment. I will invite you to follow me there."

Ando concluded less than four minutes later and turned to the judge. Javitts had asked each of the contestants, except Dr. Kline, the same two questions he had sprung on Finney earlier in the day. Ando didn't wait. "The answers are no and no, Your Honor." Then he limped back to the counsel table and took his seat.

I have underestimated my Buddhist friend, Finney realized. The little man's dignity filled the courtroom.